The Way Blood Travels

Oliver Slate-Greene

Cover Image: Camille Johnston

Cover Design: Dallas Athent

ISBN: 978-1-8381359-1-1

For my nana, Lizzy Haglund, who
always cared for me.

Goeienag slaap lekker, ek is lief vir jou.

If we can stay with the tension of opposites long enough — sustain it, be true to it — we can sometimes become vessels within which the divine opposites come together and give birth to a new reality.

–Marie-Louise von Franz

Contents

PROLOGUE: THE TEMPERATURE

I still take the temperature outside through windowsills. My right palm pressed up against the glass acting as meteorologist. The glass revealed a perfect, opaque palm print that meant my towel was going to be cold, and still damp from my morning shower.

I used to take showers compulsively. I was not excessively oily, or marred with acne, actually I had always been told that I was fairly good-looking for my type. "Unique". It was just that I had read in a Linda Goodman book on stars that as we exist and interact with people throughout the day, we pick up their magnetism. We collect ethereal pieces of metal from other peoples' beings, and carry them around as our own. All the words people say, all the thoughts they have, all of the millions of electrical signals that they produce—vibrate—and go through some kind of sublimation process such that they manifest themselves into the physical world as tiny, magnetized pieces of metal. Parasitic holism.

These exquisite magnets stay trapped in our auric fields until we wash them away. We must bathe for a whole series of hygienic reasons, of both the mental and spiritual variety.

I did fib a bit though. I also had oily ears—and I could never stand that sensation.

ON TAKING AND LEAVING

I started working at Big Bill's Gas and Auto Mechanics Shop when I was twelve years old. Peter, my father, could never remember to give me money for school, and his version of a full fridge included the entire Heinz series of comestible spreads, and domestic beer. For my twelfth birthday I asked him for the only present I would ever receive—a bicycle.

I loved that bicycle with such a tremendous amount of affection that thinking about it now makes me weepy. It meant freedom from the house, from Peter, from my middle school— those stupid kids with their regurgitated, clever words designed to sting. I would pedal as fast as I could. I liked to feel my lungs exercise oxygen into CO_2—my eighth grade science teacher was very pretty, and I loved to listen to her explain how human bodies worked. My short hair would ripple against my head. Going downhill real fast on a windy day felt like getting a hug from God.

The chain only ever popped off once—right by Big Bill's. I walked my bum bike into his garage and asked for a set of tools, and some WD-40.

"You're pretty handy with that socket wrench there, twerp."

"I'm not a twerp. I like fixing things. And my dad's always too tired. So, when something in the house breaks—I'm the one who fixes it."

Big Bill grinned. His teeth were stained from coffee and cigarettes, but he had the friendliest smile I had ever seen. Most adult men didn't smile at me and a sense of uneasiness often accompanied my male teachers when in my presence. The week before my chain broke, while ringing me up for a pack of gum— a convenience store clerk looked my body up and down, then asked if I was a boy or a girl. He seemed genuinely puzzled and concerned, as though a child was going to rob him of something. I felt naked in front of this grown man's question, and his dangerous lack of ease about the whole thing set my teeth on edge. Without answering, I left the gum on the counter and rode away.

"What's your name?" Big Bill asked, "How old are you?"

He said that if I wanted to, I could start coming in before and after school. His dad worked all the time too when he was a kid, and if I wanted to make some extra milk money it'd be fine by him.

"But I don't accept tardiness. If you say you're going to be here at a certain time, you better be here at that time. Time is a very important tool, and I want you to learn how to respect it, and maybe one day wield it properly."

Time passed at various speeds, and suddenly I was a senior in high school. Those halls that smelled like peppermint gum and never-quite-dry paint were going to be a thing of the past, and I couldn't wait. Rows and rows of ugly yellow lockers with those strange three slits on the front of them. Ventilation? I guess it is important to let books breathe, actually…

I had close to seven grand saved up by that time. I would have had more if I hadn't started paying the bills at thirteen. So that's the first thing I was taking with me whenever I got myself out of the house—my debit card. I still thought cash was king. When I applied for the account, the banker told me I needed parental consent. I knew Peter would be useless, so I asked Bill to sign instead. Bill said he'd like to help, but he didn't think it was right because he would have to forge my father's signature. And assuming another man's identity is a very serious crime. So, I forged my own father's hand. I understood what Bill was saying, but Bill wasn't aware of just how bad Peter was at caring about anything other than Peter. Because I never told him.

I loved to make lists. Making lists was something I was very, very good at. It calmed me down and opened up my brain. I couldn't control much about my life living in the house but lists afforded me a sense of control. I started keeping a list of the things I was going to take with me as soon as I was ready to leave the house. I started right after Peter punched my lights out. He only ever did it once. Actually, it may have been the only physical contact we ever had.

I woke up, and dried blood had caked the inside of my parched and sore mouth. My right cheekbone was on fire. When I came to, Peter was passed out in his recliner, beer had spilled all over his denim lap.

Figuring out what to leave is infinitely harder than choosing things to take: my teddy that my mother had given me on my fourth birthday, my books! I attached myself to things. I became parent over the inanimate. I knew they could feel, because quantum mechanics told me so. They must have a process. And I felt involved and responsible for that process being a pleasant one.

MY MOTHER

My mother died when I was seven and a half years old. After that, everything in the house smelled like camphor or mildew.

I loved the way the other kids at my school smelled like vanilla and cool air. Well, not the boys. They smelled like wet cotton, pencil shavings, and body spray. I can still smell the canister—a sickly, sweet metallic odor that sticks to the back of my throat.

My mother was unusually pretty for the Western Massachusetts town we were both born and raised in. I don't know what she died of. I don't even remember it happening. The man I called by his first name only told me she had died. I don't have any memory of her ever being sick. One day, she was just not there anymore. And peanut-butter pancakes with milk turned into cereal without.

The things I remember about my mother are small, but sacred. Her hands were always smooth and cool like paper. I used to take her hand in my little one and press it against my face. She would wake me early in the mornings, and take me on long, winding drives.

"I want you to learn how to breathe right," she'd say. "Nobody knows how to breathe anymore."

She smelled like clean laundry and shea butter. She always pointed out impossibly small tracks in the woods behind our house.

"That's the Green Man," she'd whisper to me. "You hear that?"

I bent down on my knees and put my ear to the ground.

"Yes, I hear it," I replied.

She smiled at me and patted the small of my back. "That's them. They're always making music, and the Green Man—he's always making trouble."

My mother was Bahamian, but white, and often told me how she "island hopped" when she was young. I thought that was the most magical thing I had ever heard. Her parents bought her a dinghy with an outboard motor for her fourteenth birthday. She told me how she cut up old, ill-fitting dresses and stitched together make-believe flags, writing mottos on one side of them in black sharpie. She couldn't remember what they were though. I wish she had. My desire to know what the fourteen-year-old version of my mother wrote on her flags was overwhelming, and it made my throat feel swollen when I thought about it for too long.

"I kicked and I kicked—I was a pupil of prenatal karate. Not like you. You came away easy. I didn't feel no pain with you, baby."

She used to take me by the wrist and ankle and spin me so fast, for so long, that we'd both fall down dizzy. Then we tried to walk in a straight line. Whoever fell over first was a rotten egg.

THE GIRLS' LOCKER ROOM (A MEDITATION ON CURIOUS SMELLS)

Her hands felt clammy on my waist, but I didn't mind. I cupped her left breast in my hand and took long, exacting squeezes. I spelled my name in cursive on her nipple.

Her lips on mine felt like fire. Everything about me was alive—I was vibrating. Linda Valentino (that can't have been her real name) was mine for four minutes before gym class every Tuesday and Thursday, for two months, during my sophomore year of high school. We were just babies then, mimicking the primal scene from our favorite films. Everything is an imitation of 20th Century love when you're a teenager. I moved my hand from her breast, down her ribs, to her lower stomach. I lingered there for a moment— terrified. She didn't stop me. My hand went searching for that warm place between her legs so like my own, I thought to myself in that moment—and promptly pushed aside for fear of imminent death. She adjusted her weight from foot-to-foot so that I might have better purchase. I'll never forget the shock. The wetness. The sound of her breath by my ears, and then the fifth period bell cried out. We snapped out of our mutual trance. Fused beings, linked animals—no more.

"Alright ladies, let's move it! Move it! Move it!"

It was rainy, so that meant indoor PE. Basketball or stick hockey. I liked the rain usually, but not on gym days when I had to smell everybody's sweat and food preferences. When too many bodies perspire at once, the room becomes thick with moisture. Girls have an alarmingly sweet quality to their sweat. Old honey left in the sun to bake, and then rained on—human petrichor.

The girls' locker room smelled like that, but worse. Muted farts from self-conscious females denying their own bodily functions. A chronic, lingering profusion of menstrual blood in the air. Mildewed mesh and Tilex. The girls' locker room is an unholy place of gossip. And the words that fell from cruel lips desperate to fit in clung to the steam that hung perpetually over the heads that uttered them—a hyperbolic chamber.

"Hey you!" a loud voice was directed at me, "Shouldn't you be showering with the rest of the monkeys?" It was Linda Valentino.

Linda Valentino had been accused of being a lesbo by her friends, and that wasn't good. There were no more secret meetings behind the lockers after that.

I looked down at my body. I saw hair on my legs. A little trail on my stomach.

"I'm not a monkey," I replied.

MY REAL FATHER, AND HOW TO REBUILD ENGINES

Metal, rubber, grease.

In the old days, external combustion was king. Coal, wood, oil—when lit, created steam, created motion. Travel the world in eighty days. Manifest your destiny on a cross-country train ride, be sure to ride armed, ye old passenger of yesteryear!

Internal combustion is far more efficient—less messy. Smaller. Progress. Put gasoline in a tightly compacted space—set it on fire. Now that's energy.

Four strokes in the heart of a car: intake (1), compression (2), combustion (3), exhaust (4). Sounds familiar…

When your car won't start…your engine rolls and stresses but doesn't hum. It's usually because you've got no fuel, no air, no fire. I still find that to be incredibly comforting. "No fuel, no air, no fire—no go," Big Bill said over his shoulder to me one day as he was working on an old Datsun. He laughed and threw his head back. When Big Bill laughed—the walls shook. His hands were stained a permanent, muddy gray. He will forever evoke the smell of engine oil and diesel exhaust. We took cars apart and put them back together again for years. He had me start on toasters.

"If you can make toast, we can move on to bigger things," he said only a few months into my helping out at his shop. He handed me a red toaster. "The wife was fond of that, said it performed magic on bread. So…y'know. Let's see what you can do."

It took me a month to get that damn toaster in order. It still works.

I wanted to get my hands dirty, to have oil and sweat run down my face. I wanted to lean over the hood of a car and diagnose the issue by ear when I tapped the guts with my big, silver screwdriver. I wanted to be big, smart, muscular. I wanted stained coveralls, a woman, a beer, and a huge cock that I could take out of my pants and put in things: women, mouths of strangers at bus stations, fuel tanks, pillows, light sockets. I had a phantom heat-seeking object between my legs, and nothing to do about it. I got the toaster working, though. I channeled my frustrations into my fingers and rearranged wires, and soldered little, fragile pieces of metal alloys together.

"Good work. Now this." After the toaster, he had me repair a washing machine.

"Why do we need—"

"Rags get dirty, and don't question technique."

The Maytag was a piece of cake. After that, Bill and I worked together on cars, motorcycles, trucks, snowmobiles, diesel engines. We did body work, replaced bumpers; banged metal, chrome, oil, grease; got dirty cuts, burns, and scrapes. We worked with our hands. Our minds pumping blood from our brain to the appendages of our bodies—that blood carrying messages telling us how to fix what was broken in the world. We felt confident that we could fix anything, because we felt compelled to do so. I would always stay later than Bill, who was married with two young boys. He had given me keys to the shop when I was around fourteen. During the witching hour, I played Dr. Frankenstein—at my feet, my beautiful monster that could never talk. I heard the ghosts of songs, garbled and delayed by the distance between when I first heard them and the present moment.

Bill was the closest thing I had to a father since my mother died. He didn't care that I kept my hair short, or covered my clothes in black liquids, or got cut up; but he did barber my hair, and bought me clean white shirts, and gave me band aids.

High school was absurdly easy, and impossibly boring. All the girls, and all the boys, and then me. I wasn't treated horribly by high school standards. I never contemplated suicide. I never took it seriously enough to go super dark. For all the pain, confusion, heartbreak, boredom, ennui, anxiety, physical discomforts—I knew it wasn't my life. I heard something else calling to me. I knew my life was going to be different, and therefore better, than the lives my peers were going to lead. I knew that in the world, there were an equal number of antidotes to all the dark feelings I felt as a very young person: of joy, laughter, lightness, order, greenery, splendor, mystery, wonder, excitement, change, love.

I loved the cars I worked on. I loved them so much I would clean every crevice, every scratch, every imperfection I couldn't fix—I cleaned. I talked to the cars like my peers would talk to their friends, or old ladies to their plants. I wanted my cars to grow, but it was I who was growing.

On my sixteenth birthday, Bill and his family had me over for dinner, which was not at all unusual—in fact, most nights I would crawl onto their couch after something like an eighteen-hour shift in the shop. Bill's wife Racine, who taught ballet classes at the local YMCA, would get up before dawn and make coffee, and I would join her, the two of us together in shared silence. Bill, never accustomed to waking up early, would shake his head at us and call us batshit for greeting the dawn with smiles. Then he would drive me to school. "Don't be late," he'd mumble through heavy lips as I walked up the school steps.

After we finished off the cake, Bill reached into his pocket and procured a small package. Actually, it was just newspaper that had been wrapped in tape a bunch of times. He, Racine, and the boys were all grinning like dopes as I clumsily tore at the scotch tape barrier to what I already knew to be a set of keys.

Bill walked me out to the garage where my eyes drank in the gravity of what was in front of me. Sitting there, next to Bill's F-350, was a dinky-looking heap of parts and the completely stripped body of a 1969 Mustang. The whole thing turned me on. The same feeling coursed through me when I received my bicycle four years earlier, but this time, something called a Cobra Jet engine sat inside of it. I was a little embarrassed to be feeling this type of eroticism next to my quasi-dad, but he just stood there looking very self-satisfied, his wide shoulders barely fitting in the doorframe he was leaning on.

"That'll keep you busy for a while," he said as he slapped my back.

I thanked him, thanked Racine—I think I even thanked their kids. I mumbled something about going home because my dad was going to leave work early to visit with me on my sixteenth birthday. A highly unusual occasion.

It was a complete lie. I had to get out of their house. A rising tide was forming inside of me. The entire walk home from Bill's I cried and cried. In this world, someone loved me enough to surprise me.

CONTRAST

I watched a lot of television when I was a kid. I didn't understand my peers, or them me, and neither cared. Peter had held the nightshift at the mill since long before I was born. He left early in the evening and arrived home late mornings. Our paths almost never crossed. I preferred being alone. Well, no, I wanted company, just not Peter's. He was mean, and had bad breath, and on the rare occasion that we would find ourselves sharing a meal at the dinner table—I would stare at his acne scars and watch the way his mouth squinched up as he chewed. In my whole life we probably only said a thousand words to each other. Peter was my roommate. A man who should never have had a child. If I could ask anyone, anywhere, anything: I'd ask my mother why she married such a poor example of the human race.

Before I started working at Bill's shop, working on cars, and before I found literature—would watch tiny people interact on a screen. I thought they could hear me. Dorothy Zbornak from The Golden Girls taught me how to be graceful in the eyes of sharp words from the mouths of others; Uncle Jesse from Full House taught me that you can be cool and loving; Mr. Jefferson from The Jeffersons taught me to have goals, and to believe in myself; Dan from Roseanne taught me humor; Bob Barker from the Price is Right taught me to spay and neuter my animals.

I never learned how to argue; I never learned how to cook a full meal; I never learned how to sew; how to fish; what a bedtime story was; I thought functioning families were fiction. I didn't know that the other kids weren't paying gas and electricity bills, or putting money towards a mortgage on a house that wasn't even in their names.

Other kids went home to homes. Homes whose porches would change with the seasons, and pajamas with matching sheets, and parents who asked them questions. They got to practice how to argue; how to rupture and repair; how to interact in meaningful ways; how to love.

Bill and I talked, but mostly about cars and sitcoms of the late seventies and eighties. He was like my father in the most concrete way in that—he was not my friend. We loved each other, but we weren't blood, and we weren't playmates.

And then there was Racine, who taught me how to move as though guided by spirits, who caught me one afternoon dancing alone, cutting a rug to a fast-tempo doo-wop ditty in Bill's garage as I worked. I hadn't realized I was being watched until I spun around to find her grinning at me from the doorway. She said I had a real talent and invited me to join her classes at the Y. The offer was incredibly touching and I desperately wanted to say yes, but the curves of my body embarrassed me. Racine saw this and suggested she teach me privately during my lunch hour. I immediately agreed and after a few months, I was nailing pirouettes and leading up to working on fouettés. It all felt so natural and right to me. Though it was hard to look in the mirror unless I was assessing my own technique, I learned how to be a critical observer of my body. To understand how it could impact space in beautiful ways, even if I wasn't quite embodied while doing so. I hated my breasts. The way my mid-section skirted ever-so-slightly outside the invisible lines of my shoulders. To love and to hate the same thing is a completely unique experience shared by a small community of people.

BLOOD OF MY BLOOD

I worked on my car for two years—my knuckles sore since the day I started working on her. My dream car. My Mary-Ellen. That's what I call her. I converted her into an alternatively fueled machine. Most people think that owning a veggie-powered vehicle is ridiculous but consider for a moment the sheer number of restaurants in the world—in America, in particular—that just toss the stuff out! Then consider the amount of money spent on gas. I haven't paid for fuel since I was eighteen. But that's not about this, it's about that, and I'm eighteen again.

Bill helped me apply the last coat of wax on Mary-Ellen. My very own 1969 Mustang Mach 1. Black with a tan interior. A 428 Cobra Jet backed by an automatic transmission and power steering. No racing stripes. Bill and I agreed that they were kind of dated and unnecessary. I wanted Bruce Wayne. No, I wanted the Batmobile. The first time I turned over Mary-Ellen's engine—the first time I heard her talk to me—I felt like dancing.

School was almost over and I was going to graduate with a nearly perfect average. It didn't much matter though, considering there was no money for college and I already had my vocation neatly stacked away in my back pocket. Bill and Racine offered to help me pay for community college, but I immediately declined their kind offer with gratitude.

"I really think you should reconsider," Racine said.

"Yeah, you don't want to end up like me," Bill added. Racine looked at him with so much warmth in her eyes.

"Actually," I said, putting my hand on his briefly, "if I turned out to be half the man you are—I'd consider myself lucky. No, I like cars. I just think I'd like to work on cars, keep making money, and one day open a shop of my own."

Bill looked down at his hands, "If I didn't have two other boys to think about, I'd say Big Bill's shop could be yours one day…"

I had to bite my tongue to quell the rising tide.

After Bill and I topped her off, I drove Mary-Ellen back to the house that Peter and I shared. The house I grew up in. The house that held the skeletons of so many four-leaf clovers; the house I found and lost God in; the house I had secret, sexual encounters in with boys, girls, and people in between. If I close my eyes—I can still recall the most minute details of that space. The length of the cracks in the kitchen ceiling, the pattern of the wallpaper in the downstairs bathroom, the swishing sounds my socked feet would make against the carpet on the stairs.

I closed the door of my car and the satisfying click when latch kissed striker was music to my ears. Oftentimes, I opened the door just to shut it again.

The house was completely dark when I entered. This was not unusual. The television was emanating blue light, on full volume in Peter's room. This, again, was not unusual. I decided to put a few slices of bread in the toaster (the same one I had fixed when I was twelve years old) while I went down the hall to turn off the television. When I pushed open Peter's door, his room, save all the furniture, was completely empty.

This—this was unusual.

There was a note on the top of the TV unit:

> *I paid against the house til April. I guess there isn't much to say. Good luck with all your future endeavers.*
> Peter

Back down the hallway, poorly written letter in hand, something close to disbelief went up and down my body. After a piece of perfectly-toasted toast, buttered and grape jellied, I lit the stove—gas was still on for now—and lifted the torn sheet of paper above the flame. I re-read it one last time. Memorized it for posterity's sake, misspellings and all. I spoke, "E-N-D-E-A-V-O-R-S." The sound of that dinky piece of paper disappearing into the cool atmosphere was almost as pleasurable as listening to Mary-Ellen's doors open and close.

I decided that night that I would stick around until graduation in May, when the bank was likely going to collect on the house.

Mary-Ellen, the road, and me. That thoroughfare of wanderers. A generation of lost dreamers and romantics, of vagabonds and kings of stories. The call was imminent and piercing. It cut through the fog of every-day sameness with shocking potency. Sing to me, oh Muse!

Outside in the cool night, I opened the hood of my car and the palm of my hand, and sliced the latter open with a switchblade, letting the blood drip slowly onto Mary-Ellen's engine. Steam emanated from the life running through me. I had now christened my vessel.

We were now one.

MAY

I stayed in the house for the remaining few weeks. Every day that I went to work was going to be the day I was going to tell Bill my plans, and what had already happened. Every time I sat at their dinner table, I was going to tell them about Peter taking off, and my plan to set sail for a new world. But I never did. I couldn't. I felt so guilty. I wanted to take them with me, all of them, the boys too—my surrogate brothers.

Every night I refined my list of takings. I had to adapt because of Mary-Ellen, who, though beautiful, was not overly generous in the way of storage space. I bought a tent. I cleaned out the house of all dispensable, unnecessary items. I gave pieces of furniture to Goodwill. Kitchen appliances to shelters. Books to my high school's library.

I was seeing a few people romantically during that time—the tail end of my senior year. A boy who was confused about the kind of person he wanted to fall in love with, and a girl who liked boys but hated penises. Childhood trauma? Baby queers? Childhood can be traumatic even if nothing "that bad" happens to you.

The way Wyatt's body moved was thrilling to me. In class, I loved watching him unfurl his powerful arms heavenward as he stretched himself back into the shared reality of our English class, the upper part of his giant frame lifting from his seat as he squeezed his fists into tight balls.

My world was in my head, in the resistance of a wrench against a cold engine block, in the flawless execution of a fouetté, but always above my neck—my body was just a conduit. An oxygen metabolizer, a synapse-catalyst. It wasn't mine as it belonged to the Earth and music—I just happened to inhabit it. I had no reverence for the slight rounding of my hips, which I hated to catch in the reflection of a chrome fender, and no connection to my insides other than literal blood and fascia. There was also the roundness underneath my collarbone, two question marks, the reasons I never much regarded mirrors outside of nailing technique in class.

Wyatt's body was beautiful to me in this kind of horrible, exciting contrast. Hard and dry, a series of straight lines—any roundness only deepened the sense I got of being around a man, and was located mostly on the backside. My response to him was immediate and carnal. I wanted him with my body, so I guess that meant I wanted him inside me. It wasn't difficult to coax him into bed, and my decidedly androgynous look seemed to work in my favor with this particular boy who rumors swirled around at the beginning of lacrosse season like clockwork.

Wyatt walked me home after a particularly boring day at school, and I invited him inside. By the time we reached the top of the stairs, he was already behind me, rubbing his giant hands up and down the back of my body. His hands made small threats of moving towards my chest every other sharp intake of breath—but they never did. An unspoken moment of relief passed between us. I wasn't going to make him touch me there, and he didn't really want to. I could feel him pressed against me, already strong and full in youthful eagerness. I didn't want to miss the opportunity to watch. My spirit had already exited my body, and I wanted to make sure I got what I didn't know I was looking for.

"Wyatt, slow."

His stare had a sharp, metallic quality to it, and sufficed as a very clear response.

"I'm going to enter my room. I want you to wait ten seconds then open the door."

"Okay."

"Then take off all of your clothes. Starting from the top."

The door closed softly behind me. I couldn't even feel my hands, and my heart was pounding. I breathed out slowly, walked towards the foot of my bed, and tried to soften the dizziness that seemed to wobble in and out of my consciousness.

"Now?"

"Yes, come in."

I'll never forget the acute sense of arousal I felt looking at Wyatt's body, naked and ready. It wasn't as though I didn't respond from a sexual part of me, I wanted him to come towards me, to touch me, to scratch this physical itch. But I also felt an amazing sense of embodiment flood me, when I imagined everything from out of Wyatt's eyes, from inside his body and not my own. My spirit circled back down, and without knowing what I was doing—entering Wyatt's form—I could feel everything he was doing to my body as though I was doing it myself. Mind fuck wasn't even the half of it.

I wanted everything Wyatt had. His weight, his heft, his smell. The smoothness of his chest, and the forward action he took as he greedily sought out corporeal pleasure. But the actual act itself…it was difficult to keep laughter at bay, and I liked Wyatt! I knew of his sensitivities, and had to concentrate the other half of my being on keeping cool. My split spirit and mind fought on the battleground of my body.

Fucking boys and fucking girls are two completely separate practices. Boys are rougher, more serious somehow, slightly comical in their earnest belief in the power of their aroused organs. Boys kiss angry. Girls kiss so sweet by comparison. Girls are all the hot and cool things of the earth: pain and pleasure; silence and noise. Fucking a girl is like lifting your ear to the gates of Heaven. Mysterious, because you can't see if what you're doing is working, unlike with boys. No, with girls you must develop a sixth sense. Become completely attuned to that girl's body, and that body's particular needs. You have to listen to the breath, feel the muscles around her pelvis adjust. You must lose yourself, and remain at once. Fucking girls is exhausting, exhilarating, terrifying. Fucking boys was like wrestling with myself.

Afterward, Wyatt and I shared a glass of water on the floor of my near empty house. He took out a cigarette. It was raining outside.

"May I? he asked.

I nodded.

"Want one?"

"No thanks," I said.

He shrugged and lit his cigarette. I loved the way that cigarette smelled. Like an evil forest burning.

"I'm leaving after graduation," I said.

"Me too, man. Fuck this town." Wyatt had pretty, long blonde hair and a very charming habit of shaking his side bangs free from behind his ears, just so he could put them back again. "Which college are you going to again?"

"I'm not."

"Where are you going then?" Blue smoke poured off his plump bottom lip.

"I don't really know, I s'pose."

He dragged long and hard on his American Spirit, considering what I had just said. Not that there was much to consider. Smoke rings escaped his lips. "Cool," he said.

PINE NEEDLES

After graduation, Mary-Ellen and I spent time on the road. I thought about my last days at home, how I left at five a.m., how I sat on the roof of the house all night staring up into the spring blanket of stars. I thought about my mother and her hands. I thought about all the things I had given away, and all the things I decided to take with me. I thought about Bill and Racine.

I left them a note and my old blue and red bicycle for one of the boys to use or trade or sell. The note was a list of all the things I was grateful to them for. It was a private collection of debt. Bill was the only father I had ever known and I told him that. And Racine had given me the gift of refined movement and healthful inclinations. I promised to get in touch with them whenever I was settled somewhere.

Some memories can be so sweet that they hurt worse than the sour ones. What I wouldn't give to feel the way I felt being bathed in the kitchen sink again.

Clean sheets come close though.

THE COMFORT OF ROADS (WHEN REALITY AND EXPECTATION COLLIDE)

The continental United States is a collection of roads. They may all appear to be uniform, but just as states have different names, so do their roads have different flavors.

I was on the road for only two weeks before I forgot about what it was like to be that other me.

I stopped in Detroit, Michigan, and walked into a bar. I was five foot ten and athletic, with broad shoulders. I was eighteen then and full of wanderlust. I had no responsibilities. I had money enough to keep my nose clean. I was agile and strong, and my heart ached with curiosity.

A prostitute named Louise walked up to me and asked me if I wanted to dance. I said I always wanted to dance.

In a moderately packed dive bar in Detroit—that once-faded city just coming back to life—Louise and I danced to Billy Idol, Def Leppard, and Duke Ellington. She rested her head on my shoulder during Billy Joel's "She's Always a Woman," and I felt her sadness pour out of her. I felt her immense and ceaseless longing, and it mirrored my own. She would later tell me that she came from an incredibly wealthy family who lived in California. She ran away to Detroit, of all places, because she wanted to go backwards. She said she felt like she was born wrong. I told her I was too.

She moved her hand to the front of my jeans. Startled, she took a step back from me. "Where's your dick?" she whispered.

I laughed, "It's up further and tucked back a bit."

I had been on the road for only two weeks, and here I was in a bar in Detroit getting asked where my dick was. Perfect.

Louise considered this as she sucked air through the gap in her front teeth. I liked that gap a lot.

"Do you want to get high?" Louise asked me.

"I don't do drugs," I said.

"It's just weed, you don't 'do' weed—you smoke it," she snorted.

"Oh, okay then."

We lit up in Mary-Ellen and looked out at Lake St. Clair. I was watching a tugboat pull a broken, orange water taxi against the gray clouds and clear black of the night.

"I wasn't freaked out that you didn't have, like, a big cock, you know." Louise handed me the joint. Thick, billowing clouds of white cascaded from her lips. I pressed the joint to my lips and breathed in, and then coughed until my eyes teared up. Louise was high and laughing. She hit my back. I unscrewed the cap of a water bottle and gulped the whole thing down. "You just pass so easily."

"Pass as what?" I asked, finally recovered.

"A dude."

My head started to feel light, "I'm not a dude though."

Louise took the joint nimbly from between my fingers and inhaled, "Aren't you?"

There was something in her voice, in the truly genuine tone of her smoky question that burst open a levee inside of me.

My body felt tingly, "I never thought about it, I guess."

I looked down at my chest—nothing there. I had always had small tits, but had been wrapping an ace bandage around them for so long that they were more like deflated balloons than tits. I thought about all of my various sexual encounters. I liked being fucked from behind like a gay man when I was with boys, and I liked dominating the girl beneath me. I thought about my hair that had never once grown beyond my shoulders. About the garage at the house that I filled with dumbbells and weights, and a bench to make myself bigger. I thought about how happy it made me when Racine confused my pronoun sometimes during dance class. I liked my small tits—actually, no—I liked the fact that if I had to have tits at all—that they were small. But at that moment, I wasn't sure how much I wanted them on me anymore.

We drove Mary-Ellen back to Louise's apartment. It was a small studio above a laundromat. It smelled so good. We made love for what must have been about three weeks straight. I kept my shirt on when we had sex, and she never said anything about that. She never touched my chest, but she let me do all sorts of things to hers.

When we went out, she introduced me as a boy, and we made up fake names for me every afternoon. We both had an insatiable appetite for brunch, amongst other wholesome things, subsisting on eggs and toast and avocado slices on more days than not.

Louise stopped turning tricks during our brief but potent time together, even though I didn't care either way. I think she started to fall in love with me too.

Meanwhile, my body continued to scream at me, or scream out at me is the better way to say that. But when Louise illegally procured for me synthetic male hormones, everything began to change. The second I pressed my thumb down on the plunger, the moment the needle tip slid into my upper thigh—that sensation of holy rightness encased in a yellowish oil running through my veins—that was the moment I began to feel hope: sheer, unadulterated, lucid, joyous hope.

Pine is considered a softwood. Testosterone synthesized.

My feet started to itch after around four and a half weeks. I had become used to numbers on signs, and to the clutch. I had the desire for movement, and I couldn't bear to idle any longer.

"You have to go, I guess." She pulled a needle out of my thigh. I looked at her, and then at the small spot of blood pooling from the injection.

"Yeah, I have to go," I said.

"No charge for services rendered."

We laughed. She kissed me on the mouth. "Here, take this with you." In her palm, she held the small vial from which she extracted the fluid that was now a sac in my thigh. Testosterone: Cypionate 500 mL/L. Louise told me she got it from a "friend" of hers who owed her money. She gave me a bag of needles and handwritten instructions on how to get all the air out of the tip, so that I wouldn't get any air bubbles in my bloodstream.

"You'll have to buy the alcohol and swabs as you go," she said. "There are enough needles in there to last six weeks. When you run out—just go to a safe haven place and ask for size eighteen needles."

"I'm sorry that I'm such a dude. That kinda sucks," I said. It was more honest than I intended it to be. Louise just laughed and sucked air through her amazing gap.

Later, she watched me through the window as I got into Mary-Ellen, and put her hand up to the glass. She must have been taking the temperature outside. The chilliness reminded me of a song the radio would not stop playing. Guess that's why they call it window pain.

Food on the road tastes different. You're always kind of hungry. Most people don't realize how comforting it is to have a kitchen. Before I left Louise she said, "Too bad we could never decide on a name for you," and she handed me a grilled cheese and tomato sandwich.

"I'm not worried about it. It'll happen when it happens. Thank you, Louise."

For exercise I would pull into some secluded part of whatever town I happened to be in, and I would blast the radio and dance. My body moved through space and I imagined its lines made up the tip of a brush. I painted the sky with my intentions. I danced until I soaked my shirt through with sweat. I danced to feel connected to whatever it was that made us human.

I cleaned myself in open, moving, bodies of water whenever I could. Sometimes I used sinks in public places. Sometimes, when the weather was so cold my palm left a perfect, warm imprint on the glass of Mary-Ellen—I broke into foreclosed houses (you wouldn't believe how many there were in America at the time if I told you), and slept to escape the howling winds. I dreamt the dreams of the previous occupants, only to awake confused and completely aware of my own existence, like I had been watching myself sleep all night.

Rules of the Road for the Common Vagabond

Life is about dealing with loss—its pain and wonder are both measured by the small hand of a clock as it ticks by. There are days etched into my memory, knowing Peter was in the living room drunk out of his mind, ready to unload whatever level of complicated male aggression existed between us, where I would mourn each second that ticked by knowing that this was not meant to be my life.

I had years of practice tucked away—dealing with loss of life in one sense or another. Reps. A muscle built so strongly, wrapped around my bones and organs like a fist. And now my palms and fingers, exquisitely wrapped around the steering wheel, were no longer clenched but instruments of freedom.

There was a vast, interconnected community of people like me out there. The moving folks. The un-rested, the searchers, the vagabonds, the queer and unusual. In cars, packed in vans; tramping on old, worn, leather boots; working land that never belonged to us, and living on roads that unequivocally did.

If you knew where to look, you'd see us talking to each other.

A rubber tramp kept a set of white chalk in the glove compartment, ready to strike up conversations with fellow travelers across space and time.

A capital V with two right-side up triangles on a mailbox indicated that two friendly women dwelled there and if you told good stories you'd eat for free. A rectangle with a square dot in the center warned of a brutal man and told you to stay away. A lazy U over a barn meant that you could shelter there for the evening unbothered. But when you entered towns whose road markers were littered with listless, tilted ovals—you could be sure there was nothing going on in that town, which could be good or bad depending on what you were looking for.

There were all kinds of rubber tramp camps you could find if you knew where and when to look. I visited them from time to time, loving the look of the pretty women who looked me in the eye. Small bits of my spirit returned to me with every generous and greedy glance. The fires at night, often close to raging, were so life-affirming. The most unlikely community of people who wanted nothing to do with other people in common terms, all crowded around ancient light, swapping stories and food with glorious abandon.

We all had to adhere to the triplicate, unbreakable rules that were no theft, no tire-slashing, and no gas siphoning. If you were caught, accused, and found guilty by a trial of rubbery peers— your rig would be destroyed, and you'd be banished from the pack.

On post boxes, street signs, in alleyways, dilapidated advertisements; on sides of well-worn roads; you'd hear us talking. Murmurs at first, but keep driving, walking, listening, and we'd begin to howl, holding up the mirror, as we have throughout time.

THE IMPORTANCE OF REMEDIES AND HERBS

I drove west after my time in Detroit, as all young men are advised to do. Route 66 is fine; I was just excited to be free and new. It was around this time that I started to actually lose my sense of time, replaced by the rhythm of passing road underneath me. If I happened to be passing a large body of water, I would pull over—grateful to have an alternative to gas station sinks. I floated naked underneath the moon, and told her all my secrets. My body was changing rapidly. Second puberty. My already large frame now carried an extra fifteen pounds of muscle—I added calisthenics to my daily dance exercises. My voice had cracked, and I now sounded like Bruce Springsteen—who, coincidentally enough, I had always been told that I resembled. My body was pimply, and chest hair was coming in. The peach fuzz on my face had fallen away to be replaced by a respectable amount of beard. I shaved it as often as I could. I wasn't used to the itch of facial hair.

"I want to be in love with a person who makes me happy, and understands my weirdness," I said, floating on the water, staring up into the stars, talking to the moon—so young. "Sometimes I drive for hours wondering what this person is going to look like. She's a woman; I'm pretty sure about that. I don't think I'm gay after all. I fantasize about her sliding her smooth hand down my forearm, and I see her lying next to me on white cotton. So clean." I considered the next ingredient of my cosmic pizza order very carefully, "I hope she likes dogs and cats."

The moon would always talk back to me in images. I saw long hair, and smelled strawberries. I saw graceful hands covered in rings. I saw a dog's wagging tail.

My dick had also grown an extensive amount. I had a very fun two inches. It got hard. I could jack it, and poke it in things, and it could be sucked proper.

It was my third year on the road, three years on the sweet T, three years placed between me and the house I grew up in. One spring evening, I found myself hugging the Mississippi on my way to New Orleans, Louisiana. I celebrated my twenty-first birthday in a Bayou bar that smelled like ozone and rum-soaked old wood. The bar sat at the entrance to an old bridge, and the only other people inside were salty fishermen who upon discovering it was my birthday began ordering round after round of shots.

After hours of hard drinking and stories sufficiently swapped, I stumbled out of the bar, cross-eyed. The sky opened up with a lightning crack, and rain flew down, encouraged by thick gusts that rattled the trees. I looked up to the sky hoping for a glimpse of the moon, but of course I couldn't see her through the rain. I thought I was laughing, but as it turns out, I was vomiting. I ran over to the side of the bar to clear the poison from my system, retching so hard that I ended up pissing myself, which is when I actually began laughing. Long, heaving, belly-straining gulps of laughter—allegrissimo!

With a clear head, I stood up, twenty-one. A man who had just pissed his pants on the side of the road from too much drink. Mary-Ellen sat nearly invisible in the darkness, as I launched myself over the side of the bridge into the water. Thankfully, it was deep enough to catch me without incident. I rolled around, trying my best to mimic the spin cycle of a washing machine. I kicked my legs up, and floated for some time.

To the hidden moon, "Thank you."

~

One afternoon, in late September—the air was still sort of soaked with moisture, but had the promise of cooler weather—I walked into an old, apothecary shop.

Winds of change.

A beautiful woman stepped out from behind a beaded partition holding the skull of a small animal. She placed it on the shelf.

"The winds of change are approaching," she said, as she looked me up and down. "Are you changing?"

"Constantly," I remarked.

She laughed and picked up a glass jar full of herbs. The jar mostly contained chamomile flowers, and the darkness of her skin against the white flower is an image I return to often when I feel scared.

"Are you regular?" she asked in a voice that had no business being so sexy given the content of the question.

"What do you mean?"

She had a thick, Creole accent. I could pick out her distinct smell despite the various herbs and plants of her shop. She smelled like baby powder and shea butter. She smelled so familiar!

The beautiful woman rearranged a row of scented oils on the counter so that the handwritten labels were facing out. "Do you shit after every meal?" she asked flatly.

"Oh, I see. Well, my meals aren't all that regular, but I guess I go with a certain amount of regularity."

The beautiful woman stepped out from behind one counter of the shop, and slinked over to another, where a teakettle was resting on a hot plate. "I like the way you talk."

"Thank you. I don't talk all that often." But I want to talk to you all the time, I thought.

"How come you don't eat regular?" she purred at me.

"I live in my car. Mary-Ellen."

"You live in who?" she asked, pointing her eyebrows up towards god.

I motioned to Mary-Ellen through the window.

"I see."

The woman took out a mortar and pestle and began mixing herbs.

"Are you going to take care of those?"

"Take care of what?"

She pointed to my chest with her pestle. This is how I met Natasha.

"Your tits."

I was stunned. Not because she said tits, but that she could tell!

"I shine," she said as if reading my mind.

I saw an image from my youth that had stayed with me because it was so disturbing, of a balding man with long stringy hair, and an axe through a door.

"Isn't that a bad thing?" I asked.

"Only in places that snow. When was the last time you seen snow down these parts?"

Her voice made me feel like I was eating vanilla ice cream.

"I dunno, I'm from snow."

"I know you are."

She was hard at work smashing and mashing, when she looked up to wink at me. "Some people are born happy, and some people are born sad. I was born happy. Sad don't suit me at all. Turns me an ugly color. I used to date a man who was born sad. He was perfectly nice, never once laid a hand on me, but he spoke poison." She put some of the crushed flowers and herbs in a tea bag, and turned on a hot plate with the teapot on it. She continued, "Sadness seeps out of your pores and mouth when you're sad just like a sickness. You like sad music, and sad things. All you know is blue. This man never shit. Maybe every four days he'd have a good one. He would always speak his worst poison on the third. All bad things come from our colon—that's why we need to shit to be happy. That's why it feels so good."

The teapot began to sing. Gracefully, she turned the hot plate off with her long, brown finger, and poured the steaming liquid over the mason jar filled with blended herbs.

"One day, I said 'Nathan,'—his name was Nathan—I said, 'Nathan, this is for you.'" She handed me the steaming cup. "I said, 'I know why you're spitting toxins at me all the time; lord knows you're no snake.' He said 'Why, baby? Why am I like this?' I told him: you just need to go to the bathroom more often."

I drank the tea. It was spicy, and citrusy and really, really good.

"People don't shit enough. That'll cleanse you."

She poured herself a cup.

"I don't think I'm sad," I said, letting the vapors climb up my nose. I was considering the fact that another woman was helping me along my journey. Or maybe I'm reflecting on that now. Hopefully, I was thinking about it then too.

"No, no…not sad…but you ain't happy." She looked at me for a long time. "I like your smile."

I wasn't smiling.

"I want to be happy," I said, as the sides of my lips turned upward ever-so-slightly into some version of a grin.

"That's good."

Natasha and I drank the shitting tea together. When she asked me if I wanted to stay for a while, I said, okay. She asked me how old I was. I said twenty-one. She said "Okay." She was thirty. She said she knew a doctor who could take my breasts away.

I said, "Okay."

SHAMAN

"Baby, do you know what a shaman is?"

I was doped up out of my head, my chest hurt so bad.

"Yes, I know what a shaman is," I replied.

I was leaned up against a pile of pillows, and it felt like I had a very angry goblin crouched on my chest. It wasn't pain necessarily; it was weight. It was the complete absence of pain, the numbness, that weirded me out in the lucid periods between codeine and chamomile doses. Natasha was somehow everywhere at once during my recovery. At the kitchen stove, beside me holding my hand, minding the shop—her capacity for care and presence was remarkable.

Her doctor friend turned out to be a nurse at the local clinic, who had a sister who was now a brother who owed Natasha money for the remedy she cooked up for him that would make his dick harder without any nasty side effects. So, he gave me a "good deal." My tits were small enough that liposuction could do the trick. The doctor then told me the story of how his brother lost a nipple during his subcutaneous double mastectomy. The one that survived the grafting procedure became numb to the touch or alternatingly far too sensitive. The left one they tattooed on. Apparently, his brother is married now with kids somewhere in Wisconsin, and happy, according to his brother, the doctor.

"Do you know what makes a shaman a shaman?" she asked me, in a vaguely accusatory tone.

"Don't the people send the would-be shaman out into the world to learn the secrets of the wind?"

"I do love the way white folks put spins on things sometimes..." She saw the way I looked back at her blankly, "That's me being facetious, baby."

The liposuction procedure was performed on Natasha's foldout couch on December 1st. Two days later and I was still bandaged up. You could see the bruise extending down from my chest and over my ribs.

"What is it then?"

Natasha crawled over to me and began unwrapping my bandage. I tried to push her away as I winced, but I could hardly lift my arms I was so sore.

"Hush now, we have to clean you up," she whispered.

She slowly, carefully, continued unwrapping me and my flatness, while humming a sweet lullaby.

"What makes a shaman a shaman," Natasha began as she put some witch-hazel in a mixture with water, and began to clean my bloodied nipples where the incisions were made. I could tell that I was going to scar, but my nipples were small and my chest looked good.

The outside of me was beginning to mirror my insides every day.

"It's true that some of the people would send their medicine men out into the world, alone, to dream dreams—but some didn't. It don't matter." She brushed my nipple the wrong way and my entrails moved inside me as my spine tingled. "Sorry baby. It'll get better, I promise you that." She placed fresh gauze, coated in petroleum jelly, over my sore chest, and wrapped me back up in a much lighter bandage. "The mark of a true shaman is threefold: number one: a secret, number two: scars, and number three: a new name."

The water rolling down my chest felt good. She kissed my nose. I wanted to cry then, but it appeared as though I had forgotten how.

THAT WHICH WE CALL

"Charles," she said.
I cringed.
"Noah," I said.
She laughed.
"Simon," she shouted.
I slapped my forehead.
"Edgar," I whispered.
She pointed her thumbs downward.
"Ranger," she laughed.
I blinked.
"Tristan," I proclaimed.
She shook her head.
"Amos," I declared.
She pondered.
"Felix," she offered.
We both laughed.

My list of possible names filled up eight pages, front-to-back, in my journal.

What's in a name?

Amongst those we consulted were psychics, soothsayers, local hoodoo witch doctors, Yoruba priests, poets, artists, musicians, doctors, teachers, lawyers—no one could tell me what name they thought I looked like, except one crazy, old, homeless lady who shouted at me, "Leopold! Hey Leopold! Fuck you, you limey bastard, you still owe me twenty-five bucks!"

We bought her lunch and gave her all the paper money we had on us. This lady told us about growing up in the heart of the bayou. She claimed that she could speak to animals, and that she communed nightly with the cockroaches of New Orleans. She knew everybody's secrets. She corrected our assumption that she was unhappy being homeless, and told us that she long ago rejected the way evil people do things. And then she spat into the air and laughed for a long time. She felt very holy to me. She said, "If you lay your head down on the ground for long enough—you begin to see things sideways."

Natasha and I walked home (Mary-Ellen slept in the garage during my New Orleans years). I was twenty-two, and still didn't have a name. I was tallish and well-built with muscles that kneaded over all the places people liked to see muscles knead. I had an eternal five o'clock shadow, and large, veiny hands. I was too delicate still for a name like "Frank" and not German enough for the recommended "Leopold." I needed a name that would encapsulate my best qualities, and protect against the same.

"I got it!"

One fine, hot evening, as we were swimming in the Gulf—it happened. The moon was out, and we were whispering to each other still; but this other body that held the soul of someone I cared for so deeply was talking now too. She swam over to me and whispered in my ear what was to be the name I would forever be called. It would turn my head for the next sixty years and fill the void of the twenty-two that had already come before it.

"Yeah," I nodded. "I like that. That's good."

Modal verb: an auxiliary verb that expresses necessity or possibility:

Will.

~

Natasha and I stayed together sharing that apartment above the apothecary for a long time. She taught me about trees and plants, and the benefits of eating small meals throughout the day. I suppose I taught her about literature and music, and told her stories about my time on the road. We cooked many vegetables together, and climbed hills on weekends. We made love most nights, and on some delightful afternoons. We shared a wild heart that beat rapturously against our shared chests during moments of ecstasy. Our hearts beat electric. We started to merge. We wore the same color shirts, and began to finish the other's sentences. A magical number. Then Saturn came for me.

'Your eyes that were never once weary of mine
Are bowed in sorrow under pendulous lids,
Because our love is waning.'

And then she:
'Although our love is waning let us stand
By the border of the lake once more,
Together in that hour of gentleness
When the poor tired child, Passion, falls asleep.
How far away the stars seem,
And how far is our first kiss,
And, ah, how old my heart!'

'Ah, do not mourn,' he said.
'That we are tired, for other loves awaits us;
Hate on and love through unrepining hours.

Before us lies eternity, our souls
Are love, and a continual farewell.'

— Ephemera, William Butler Yeats, 1889

We were laying down on a Victorian-era, crushed velvet, chaise lounge. It had golden lion-claws for feet. Natasha was playing with my hair, as I read her poetry. During all of our time together she had done most of the talking. That's not to say that I didn't enjoy the listening; in fact, I preferred it. My jaw would often get tired after a paragraph worth of sentences. Natasha was a natural-born talker. She was a natural-born many things: talker, healer, artist, friend, lover, witch, and goddess. I used to love the way her lips would form the shapes of vowels. I heard once that vowels carried history, and consonants reflected personality. Natasha's history was sensuous.

"Your Saturn's come back." She stopped petting my hair. "I want a family, and you're just a sprout. You got a late start on who you are."

I put my book down. "I am." I sat up. "I did."

"It's okay, isn't it?" she asked so tender. Sometimes I still talk like her.

I looked at her, searching her eyes for any drop of cruelty or malevolence to use against her when I thought about her in the future. "It is," I said, and found none. We continued our conversation late into the evening. It was a going over of all the sweet, small, poignant moments of connection we shared over the years—an elegy. The conversation then veered away from the tender, soft parts into the harsh shadow that Saturn now cast on our shared reality. A shadow that called for separation. Finally, we crashed, and slept well into the early hours of the next day.

As the sun came up, Natasha made me tea. The same tea I had that first day, so long ago, on the eve of our brilliant shared time together. I walked into the garage. Mary-Ellen was still there. Of course she was, but part of me hoped in some perverse way that she wouldn't be. My wish to stay young, to stay with Natasha my teacher and lover forever was overwhelming. I could feel my entrails turn inside as a cold menthol sensation ran through me. I felt angry, with absolutely no direction for that anger to run towards. Mary-Ellen was covered in an inch worth of sun dust, leaves, and ivy. I spent the afternoon cutting away the plants—wiping off the dust of time past, accepting my newest loss, and holding on to thoughts of the road. My always home. A never-ending collection of plus marks, and crushed, paved stone. My body began to warm, I could feel my blood thaw and pump and hum again with each layer of time removed from Mary-Ellen's body.

It was dark by the time I put my key (my key!) back in Mary-Ellen's ignition. I spun my hand to the right, and pulled out of the garage that did funny things with time.

Natasha was waiting outside underneath the faint orange light of the gas-lit lamp. She had never looked so old, had never looked so beautiful.

I wanted to cry then, but I had forgotten how.

"This is for you," she handed me a bag of the crushed flowers and leaves. "You've been doing so well all this time. Pooping-wise, I mean."

We laughed. We embraced.

A tear left a streak down the right side of her face, "You will never see me again, Will." And she winked at me.

I drove into that good night.

WHY I BELIEVE IN REINCARNATION

Energy can never be lost, only transferred. We dance, and shake, and feel. We howl at the moon and grow from weeds to trees. We sail lightly from windowsills to dark, wooden desks—floating on sunlight. We writhe in underground tunnels of our own invention. We share one mind, but exist separately, working together towards a greater purpose. We sing songs, and sting skin. We swim through frozen streams then are slaughtered by our own hands for warmth. We follow heat. We seek out light, oxygen.

I refuse to believe that it's possible for the energy trapped inside of our skin to just disappear as our bodies will inevitably.

Natasha will never die.

She will survive the Earth's eventual destruction as it gets pulled into the gravitational field of the Super Giant we knew as our Sun—that creator of all things. On the eve of its death, thirteen billion years from now, Natasha will welcome the light, become bathed in it, naked and willing. She will start a new colony of humans—Children of the Sun—and they will dance. Their eyes will never know darkness other than the rich tones of their skin and hair. They'll collect water from Europa, the frozen moon of Jupiter, and eat space creatures.

And when the Sun finally meets its own creator—God? god?!—and explodes into one million colors of celestial energy, the galaxy will open its mouth for the Children of the Sun, and suck them into a massive black hole that will spit them out on the surface of a much cooler planet.

A blue planet filled with colors much more varied than the oranges and yellows of their ancient, familial home—but these children will learn new ways of being. They will learn about the other creatures, work alongside them, eat them, and be eaten by them. They will figure out how to navigate the blue parts of their new home; how to utilize them to power and flush things away back into the same source. And the children of the Children of the Sun, with all their new and varied pigments, will look up into the bright sky, and let the light from the comforting, familiar Sun—bathe their faces. And they will smile, unsure of why it feels so good.

THINGS NOBODY TOLD ME ABOUT LOVE

For two years, I never stopped to take up with a girl for more than a night after I left the Delta—my heart was too tender after Natasha. I had been up and down, left and right—an impossible number of times. The road again was home. I would stay up for seventy-two hours straight—driving. I would get into zones so deep and haunted that I smile wide thinking back on them now. At the time, I knew that I'd wish for those moments back at some unknowable date in the future. Preemptive nostalgia was always at play during that chapter of my life.

When I would get manic like that, Mary-Ellen drove for the both of us. Her smooth gait spinning millions of tiny pieces of dirt and rock out from behind her rear tires as she went. I heard orchestras play for only me on those wheels, in those moments, on those roads. So. Empty. I banned radio during those times. I peed into old bottles through a baby medicine spoon whose tip I had cut off which allowed me to pee standing up.

I liked to feel parts of my body go numb and come back to life again in my bucket seat. I touched my shoulders, my knees, my thighs, my dick. I squeezed myself at eighty miles per hour. I loved myself completely at that speed. And then I'd crash. A wave of exhaustion would take control of every joint and sinew, every white and red blood vessel in my body would yawn. I'd pull over on the side of some nameless, but totally lovable road, and sleep deep sleeps. I would dream very dream-like dreams. It was during one of these dreams that I met Owen.

Maybe it wasn't a dream. I guess you have to be awake to meet someone, but I had seen him in a dream—I was sure of that much at least.

"Howdy!" a friendly voice boomed.

Where am I? I looked to my right, at Mary-Ellen's empty passenger seat, and picked up the newspaper. "April 22nd Bloomington Harold." I would always pick up the most widely circulated newspaper of whatever state I was in—a habit that proved useful, time and time again. It must have been April 24th-ish. I looked at my dashboard. Noon. I was driving northwest on I-90 for what I supposed was thirty hours straight.

Montana?

"I'm sorry, but would you be so kind as to tell me where I am?" I asked the stranger.

He knocked his cowboy hat back to reveal his forehead, and leaned on the windshield of Mary-Ellen. "One of those nights, huh? I had one of them myself. At least you had the presence of mind to sleep it off. It would appear as though I've lost my car somewheres between Red Lodge and Absaoarkee. Oh, and you're in Roscoe, Montana. See?" He pointed at a single, bald-faced yearling chewing its cud not eight feet away and on the other side of a charming-looking fence. It relieved itself, and then the fat creature walked away from the two men who were staring at it. I thought I heard it giggle.

"And I'm Owen." He stuck his hand through the rolled down window. Mary-Ellen smarted momentarily. No one but me had ever been inside her in years, and here this country bumpkin was penetrating her with his big meaty paw. He smiled and had shiny, white teeth. I always thought that if you took care of your teeth — you cared. I shook his hand—firm and confident—and patted Mary-Ellen's wheel to reassure her. It's okay, baby.

"Will," I said. "My name is Will. But hold on a minute…you lost your car?"

"Yeah, but I don't care," Owen said as he spat dust out of his mouth.

"You lost your car, and you don't care?" This threw me for a loop.

"Geez, is there an echo out here?" And he laughed maniacally at his own joke.

"I don't talk much," I replied. "Sometimes I have to repeat what people say to me to get back into the swing of…things."

"Well, alright!" he whooped. Owen pointed at my forehead, "You're leakin' from the top there, bud."

I put my hand to my brow and wiped away a dewy dream-induced sweat. "That'll happen I suppose. Do you want to go look for your car?" I asked this loud, friendly person who looked to me like Paul Newman crossed with Leon Trotsky, except that he was five foot seven on a good day. Owen would always say that everyone was the same size lying down, and that women loved compact things. I thought that was a really stupid thing to say, but Owen was always saying stupid things. He had wild, blond hair that sat on his head in upwardly-sprouting curls. His eyes were so blue they made you want to cry. His cheekbones so high, they seemed like they could cut glass.

"No, fuck it. I hated that piece of shit car. Not nearly as pretty as the wheels you're sitting on. Hot DAMN! What I wouldn't give to make love to this here black beauty!"

See? Stupid things.

It felt like I hadn't laughed since my lazy, New Orleans days with Natasha.

I invited Owen inside of Mary-Ellen, who had eased up a bit. He planted his butt squarely in the bucket passenger seat, and told me he "wasn't no scrub." I started the car. He hadn't bothered to move the Bloomington Herald before he sat down, and reached under his ass between his legs to pull out the paper. I thought that was a great deal of energy wasted, but Owen had energy to spare—that much I had gathered from the start.

"Indiana is America's purgatory," he told me as he tossed the paper to his feet, and looked at me squarely. "Will-y. I say you and me go get some chow and a spot of coffee, and that we get ourselves over to the Lazy EL ranch to get hired."

I considered this as Owen turned the radio knobs, waiting to hear a song that would make his knees "really bob."

I really loved that country, Montana—rolling hills of tall grass and mountains that looked like God was punching through the dirt with a closed fist. Horses who kept their noses to the ground so they could tell secrets to the Earth.

"We would make a fine pair of handsome ranch hands up the EL. I know they're looking for strong ones," he said.

I realized I hadn't eaten proper in what felt like a month, "Let's go to a diner." I was dying for some eggs and maple syrup. "I don't know how to be a ranch hand."

"It's easy! I'll teach you," Owen reassured me.

"What would we do?"

"Well, actually, do you know how to cook?"

I thought back on my childhood, alone in the house, "Yeah, I guess I do."

"Great! 'Cause I know they're wantin' a wrangler to mind horses and livestock, and a cook to mind the eggs of chickens. A you," he extended his pink index finger toward me, "and a me! Wait, no, reverse that order." Owen slapped his bobbing knee and laughed out of the window. He had the most infectious energy. When you were around Owen you couldn't help but feel like something really amazing could happen at any given moment.

I know now that there are all kinds of love in this world. The way I loved my mother will be unlike the way I love anybody else in my whole life. I felt a little resonance during those moments with Natasha, but I loved Natasha in violent and beautiful ways—I adored every part of her, and would kiss these parts like a lover, sometimes like a brother, sometimes like a friend, and sometimes like a father. I love my father in a sense. It's not quite the right word, the love is hollow—it stops where it starts, but there is a level of yearning that can only signal love. Bill, I loved completely: as a teacher, a mentor, my guide of gears and fuel and fire. Racine, I loved at first through osmosis, and secondly as my instructor in the art and science of shared silence. Owen, I loved instantly. As my equal, as my foil, as the extroverted piece that could carry my anger and conversations when I needed him to. He was X as I was O. He taught me about horses, and weather, and told me what it was like to ejaculate life from the very place you piss out of.

That afternoon, in a homesteaded-cabin-turned-diner in Red Lodge, Montana, I had the most delicious cup of coffee. Yes, as black as a moonless night for those of you who are wondering.

"In tantra they say that the cisgendered male has more to lose during sex because he gives away his prana—his life force," I said, marveling at the depth we had already arrived at somehow.

Owen slapped his thigh, "But dern it feels good to give it away!"

"You're missing my point, Owen."

"No, I bet my last shiny penny that you're better in bed cos you can fuck forever. Like a woman. You fuck like a woman! And I'm jealous of you for it." He breathed in, "Women love so deep."

I looked at him, "When you found out I was different in that way, did it spook you?" Owen and I asked each other all sorts of vulnerable, scary things.

"Sure sounds like you got something going on down there to me...minus the family jewels, of course. But I'll be honest. At first it was a wild idea because I ain't never happened on a person like you who was born against the blueprint—but now it's just a fact of you, like your brown hair, or your hairy-ass knuckles."

Owen was from a small corn town in Nebraska. The morning we met he had been on a bender with friends he used to rodeo with in college. He had three semesters of Animal Husbandry under his belt, but when his buddy told him about the ranch in Montana that needed hands, he stole his ex-football coach's broke-down Jeep and drove north. That coach would later be tried and found guilty of sexually assaulting one third of the college's football team. Owen played wide receiver. We rarely talked about that.

Never a moment more beautiful or expansive have I seen since the mornings I'd watch light stretch across the sky in Montana. Around five-thirty a.m., the stars would fade into an inky blue, after which a blaze of purple and orange blanketed the tops of mountains. The crescendo of light, as the sun came over the tree line was a most satisfying vision to behold. The Lazy EL was nestled between the Beartooth Mountains, and the West Rosebud River. I saw the best sunrises between those two ancient places.

Five a.m. rise and shine. Shower. Towel off and dress, making sure not to wake Owen. Pop in two slices of toast. Make a pot of coffee. And watch the black feeling of night dissolve into the medley of light and meaning in the morning.

I ate my lightly-buttered, heavily-jammed toast on the porch, getting a morning word in with the moon.

"Thank you," I whispered up at her. "Now, drive your golden chariot across that velvet road, Helios! I'm ready now."

Our cabin was made out of oak. It had one bathroom with a clawfoot tub, a small kitchen with a British sink, two big windows, and a coffee table. We bought a radio and a portable television to watch baseball games on. I bought a typewriter, which I kept underneath my bed. A wood-burning stove heated our slate floors in the winter, and made our water boil year-round. A huge window sat facing the western side of the world, for extra insulation in the winter as well. We alternated chores, and grocery responsibilities were split evenly. We played music all the time. Owen on his guitar—me on pots and pans. We would get stinking drunk, and shoot off tin cans on fence posts. When one of us was getting laid, the other would slink off and sleep in the barn.

Owen was head cowboy. He cared for the well-being of a remuda of horses, and looked after two hundred head of cattle. He loved those animals with all of his heart. I was scared of horses at first, but I love them now. It's all about how you approach them—always from the right side—and controlling your fear. I was the cook, and took care of the grounds. I also took care of everything on the ranch that had an engine. Our boss was named Henry. He was an old, old man, and his family had been on that land since before Montana was part of the United States of America. Henry claimed half Lakota heritage, and boasted that his "great-great-great-grandpappy kneed Custer in the balls before Custer slit his throat with a knife."

Henry mostly kept to himself on the other side of the ranch. But some nights, mostly during the winter—Henry would saddle up his horse (his horse!) and ride down to our cabin to visit with us over a bottle of Canadian whiskey.

"I don't care who the fuck your pappy was, the only whiskey that'll plant sprouts on your chest hails from Canada. Just like the only beef you ever need be putting in your gut must be Montana beef." He pulled on the bottle. "Speaking of which, my bellybutton is about kissing my spine right now—you boys have any feed?" Owen couldn't understand why and never remembered that I didn't eat the flesh of other creatures. Very annoying.

I got up and started making us all breakfast for dinner as the two men continued getting drunk in the dead of winter. Seven degrees Fahrenheit outside, and toasty-warm in our small, lovely cabin. The stove burning evenly and reassuringly through the wood that Owen and I had gathered, chopped, and arranged in a pyramid out back the summer past. I looked at Owen and Henry, and again wished I could remember how to cry. I was so overcome with love and respect, admiration and acceptance.

"God bless bacon!" Henry said.

"Amen!" chimed in Owen.

They discussed the consistency of the prolapsed uterus of the mare that had given birth earlier that day. The mare was certified, and always foaled beautifully, but on this particular day Owen had to call Henry down to assist while he doctored the exhausted and dying horse. I listened as Henry sung Owen's praises, "He didn't let her give up," he said. I could see Owen giving that horse his ebullient energy, infusing her with his magic and saving her life. Owen could do that sort of thing.

I loved going to work. Actually, that's not exactly the way to say that. When you live in the same place you work—you have one life. I loved being alive there. Existing in a place of beauty makes your life a beautiful place to exist. I cut the grass, sitting atop the world's loudest, most powerful John Deere mower. It made my teeth chatter something awful when I let my jaw rest. I made breakfast, lunch, and dinner for Owen, Henry, and the day workers, of whom there was a constant, but usually predictable rotation.

One of the day worker's McNab Border Collie had given birth to a litter of puppies underneath the cookhouse porch one morning. Three girls and a boy.

"The boy's a dern runt," the day worker said. He spat a loogie large enough to disturb the dirt, "Guess'll just tek him out back after chow n shoot'im. Won't get no money for a runt like'im."

"Please don't do that. I'll gladly take him."

"N'whydya want a no-nothing runt like'im for?"

My dislike for this person was profound. "You couldn't possibly know if he's a runt or not as he's just a puppy."

The day worker sneered at me, "Tha'sa stupidest fuckin thing I'ver heard in my whole fuckin life. Ya might could be retarded, Will." There was no delineation between his neck, beard, and chest hair. He said my name with a heavy, thick tongue. It sounded like he was saying "Whew," like he was too lazy to finish what he had started. He led me outside to the porch, and grabbed the pup by the scruff of his neck. The puppy made whimpering noises. His eyes were shut tight, but it looked to me like he was smiling.

"Don't puppies need to drink from their mom for a while?" I inquired, already knowing the answer.

The day worker spat out yet another brown, tobacco-saturated loogie, "Whew, he bet'r be ready to be wean'd quicklig, this is 'r last day in these 'ere parts. Off souf to Wyomink."

I brought the puppy home—neglected my chores for an entire day and figured out the best mixture of milk and vitamins to give my new dog.

About two months after I got him, now fully weaned off of formula and eating puppy chow (with sometimes, secret bits of bacon from Owen) we both got into Mary-Ellen. We drove for three hours up the winding hills of a mountain. Me and my runt dog, opening our mouths wide to release the increasing pressure on our ears.

It was early spring, and freezing cold when we stepped outside at the top of the world. I scooped him up in my arms, and stuffed him in my coat, underneath my shirt above my heart. I looked up at the moon, my forever Mother, and said, "Moon, we need a name."

The moon showed me images of all my favorite television, film, and radio stars from the past. I saw titles of books like Great Expectations, Wuthering Heights, and Shane dance before my eyes. I saw gyrating hips of male pop stars from the middle part of the century prior.

"But, he's not like that. He's completely unique."

The moon winked at me and shone bright on the miles and miles of road stretching out in front of me.

Miles, my puppy, slept on my lap the whole way home.

DANCING AWAY FROM CENTER

We were fully grown men now. We were getting dressed in our finest denim shirts and black Levi's. We polished our boots with saddle soap, and sat our hats on our heads so they'd correctly indicate our intentions for the evening. Owen pushed his hat back when he was feeling friendly, and forward when he wanted to be mean or mysterious.

We drove to the Griz full of still-youthful piss and vinegar. We wanted to savor that thunder in our bones, we didn't know how much longer we'd have it for. After all, we were young boys no longer. Though, I suppose I never was one, and Owen always would be.

Everyone within a 50-mile radius of the EL Ranch would go to the Griz to let loose, blow off steam, eat, imbibe, be merry, meet people to fuck or fall in love with. It wasn't particularly compelling as far as fare or venue was concerned, but it was the only game in town which made it so much more special. If it had been up to Owen, we would've gone every single night, and twice on Sunday, but we only had one vehicle between us, and no one drives Mary-Ellen but me—not even Owen. The one-time Owen and I ever fought was over Mary-Ellen. He was jealous of her, maybe?

Owen and I were leaned up against the wood bar, elbows perched on the bronze-lined rim watching the people dance. It was the busiest I had remembered seeing it, and there was a promise of something in the air.

Then I saw Owen push his hat forward, and grin his half-grin.

She was walking towards us, skillfully dodging the twirling dancers in the center of this little universe. All five feet ten inches of her coming ever-closer. My height exactly.

She had long, wavy brown hair, and dark, dark brown eyes. Almost black. Just like mine. She had delicate, small hands and a very rich voice.

"Hi."

"Howdy!" Owen flicked the top of his hat back as a flourish, from mysterious to convivial in no time.

"That was cute, pard. My name is Amy."

"Well, I sure am pleased to meet you, Ms. Amy. May I?"

She looked confused as Owen reached for her hand, and brought it up towards his face. I couldn't believe this was happening in front of me. I was embarrassed by this earnest and sudden show of intimacy. Owen stopped to search Amy's face for approval before he kissed her hand to seal his salutation. She appeared illuminated by the gesture.

"And what is it that you do, Amy?" Owen asked—already a worshiper. "Besides come up to strangers at bars I mean."

"Me?" She downed the rest of her drink, and pushed Owen's water away from him as she grabbed him by the collar that he had spent so long pressing.

"I dance," she said.

Have you ever watched two souls blend into one another like spilled gallons of differently colored paint? Roy Orbison provided the backdrop against which I watched another loss occur.

Owen and I belonged to each other for over seven and a half years. But love sometimes can only stretch so far before it stretches past its recognition. It's like your favorite song. You know that song inside and out, every note, lyric, and chord. You wake up singing it and it comes into your favorite dreams. You listen to it again and again, remembering what it felt like when you first heard it. The shapes and colors you saw when you closed your eyes. You know it so well, but nothing new can be revealed of it.

Amy, standing slightly over Owen, looked at him the way Natasha looked at me so many moons ago. And Owen looked slightly up at her, his blue eyes dancing like his two left feet. Owen danced away from me and towards Amy. Towards a first kiss and held secrets. He danced towards merging, a shared space, and agreed-upon mattresses; towards linen closets, his 'n' her towels, and rings. Towards vows—words with a little extra kick to them. I would be there to watch him kiss the bride. Owen danced towards minivans and a desk job, a salary and security, towards summer camps and parent-teacher meetings.

I slept in Mary-Ellen the night Owen and Amy met. They didn't fuck. Actually, I don't know if they did or not. Owen went home with Amy, so there was no way to be sure, and I never asked because—what difference does that make? I just needed my car. I needed Mary-Ellen. And she needed to know that we would soon be stretching our legs again.

Owen was gone, and the roads must have been repaved by now.

THE WAY BLOOD TRAVELS

Up and down and back and forth. Highways of longing. A song from my youth came on the radio, the morning I left the Lazy EL ranch. The band used to go by the name One Fell Swoop, but there was a lawsuit and now they're called something else. One fell swoop. They sing of bones like iron, and blood so heavy it's like mercury—sinking in.

Sinking into what though?

No matter.

I wrote Owen a note. It was short, but I have always been a man of few words. I told him I would try my damnedest to come and visit with him and Amy once in a while. I told him he was a good Dean to my Sal. He asked me what I meant by that once, I laughed and gave him my copy of On the Road—an old, tattered thing. His son has it on his bookshelf now—begging to be read. I told him that I didn't think I would ever meet anyone like him again. I thanked him for his friendship. I told him I liked Amy.

I put the envelope on the coffee table, and made a pot of coffee—damp towel hanging over my bare shoulders. I ate my toast and looked at Owen. He smiled when he slept. I got dressed and lugged my one suitcase out to Mary-Ellen—Miles at my heels.

"Where do you think you'll go next?"

Owen was standing on the porch, shirtless. The orange light hitting his eyes—making them impossibly blue.

He never looked so young, never looked so beautiful.

"I didn't mean to wake you," I called out to him softly, so as not to offend the morning light.

"Fuck you, you didn't wake me up. I set my alarm." Owen walked down the one step, from porch to earth. We were on the same level—we always had been. "I know you, friend," he said.

"You do. That's a funny feeling for me."

"Don't you reckon you ought to be finding yourself a nice filly to curl up next to? Seems to me you keep wandering around the way you been, you're more than likely to end up dying with only that car to leave your belongings to."

See? Stupid things: Filly.

I looked up at the dawn settling in over the white cap of the mountains, "I suppose."

Owen whistled, "Boy, you have got to have more wanderlust in you than there are stars in the sky."

Miles was already tucked away in Mary-Ellen, but he came out to say goodbye. Owen got down on his knees and embraced him for a very long time.

"You take care of him now, Miles. It's all up to you."

Miles licked his nose lightly and went back to Mary-Ellen where he curled up. He knew two grown men with as much love between them as Owen and I needed their privacy when saying goodbye. Dogs know these kinds of things.

"I'll see you later."

"Yeah, I'll see you later."

We shook hands. Owen turned to go inside; his arms crossed over his chest.

I turned towards Mary-Ellen, and those freshly paved black roads.

UNTITLED

Miles and me and the road.

I knew some things for certain by this point in my life, hovering around thirty-six: I preferred cold and dry to hot and humid; ate garlic to ward off evil spirits; kept a dill plant for luck; spring water is the best water to drink; being true to yourself is hard, and changing somebody else is even harder—and you should always do one and not attempt the other. Own animals, be good to everybody, and your own especially. Remind children that they have magical powers, and can speak to dragons, and that they are loved.

Miles and I traveled every highway, most routes, and truck loads of backroads together. We camped in deserts, and made fires the ol' fashioned way—with sticks and well-timed breath.

One evening, Somewhere America—an old man appeared out of thin air.

"Are you a ghost?" I asked.

The old man had beautiful gray hair that fell over his broad shoulders. He was wearing faded blue jeans and a tan work shirt. He carried a backpack made out of deer hide, sinew, and brass. "Your dog doesn't seem to think so," he said.

It was true, Miles sat completely at ease next to me. Only his copper-colored eyebrows moved. The man asked me if I had any food—that is when I knew for certain he couldn't have been a spirit—hungry ghosts don't attempt satisfaction. I shared with him some of my beans and coffee. We shared a long, undulating silence. The only sounds were that of our lips sipping the warm liquid, and the sweet crackling of the small fire.

"So not to completely tug on any white-person-as-culture-robber heartstrings you may carry, but...well, has anyone ever said you have the mark of a shaman?" he asked as he pointed to my hands through sips of coffee.

A funny sort of feeling took over me then, "What do you mean?"

"Do you mind if I smoke?"

I said of course not, and he pulled out a honeycomb pipe. There was something so wildly familiar about this man—but in a quick sweep of my memory, I could pull up nothing that matched his physical attributes.

"Ceci n'est pas une pipe," he said as he lit it. The old man remarked that my fingers were longer than my palms. "That," he said, "is the tell-tale mark of a shaman where I'm from."

Something came over me...I told him my story. I told him about my past. He listened intently, chewing on the end of his pipe, and spitting out alternating, brown globs of tobacco and resin. He kept his eyes straight on the fire. The only time he looked at me was when I first mentioned Natasha's name. I told him about Louise, the sandwiches and needles.

"If you were Indian, we'd call you Two-spirited," was his one remark after revealing my past to him. "But you're not—so don't do that."

He chewed on his pipe. I turned around to adjust the angle of the wood I was leaning against, and when I looked back up—he was gone. Moments later, he just appeared again. Apparently, popping in and out of the ethers came naturally to this man. He held out his palm.

"Take this," he said. "I'll look after your camp and your dog."

He held out a greenish-brownish, dried up looking flower.

"It's not an Indian custom mind you. I'm just an old hippie, who walked a different path. But this has helped me." He read the hesitance on my face. "Dream dreams. Walk until the trail of your destiny is revealed to you. Don't be afraid. Your dog trusts me—you can trust me too."

I heard a great, resounding laughter follow me as I began to walk in that ancient, haunted place.

The only thing I remember concretely is walking back to camp. My memory of the events of that evening...of the things I saw, and the secrets that were revealed, seem to have aged with time, as I was a much younger man then. And the things that are mysteries to young people, in time, become either unimportant, or solved. The old man kept his word for as long as he could.

When I got back to the circle, I found him dead. On the top of my left hand, written in big black ink were the words:

Life Is Cyclical

Only Circles Matter

I didn't even know I had brought a pen with me.

I loaded up Miles into Mary-Ellen, and we drove into town to report the death of a ghost. The police officer was none-too-pleased when we arrived back at camp to find no body lying on the ground. He lowered his sunglasses over his crooked nose, and they squished the tops of his plump cheeks down into little half-moons, "What are you playing at, son?"

If I had to guess, I would've said that the man watched far too many John Wayne films as a youth. I did not like him. I looked at the empty campsite, "I don't understand, I checked his pulse…"

The police officer wrinkled up his man-baby face and spat into the hot, dry desert at his feet. "Well, at least you got me out of that damned station." He was gone, headed back towards his station of contempt before I could respond.

I turned towards Mary-Ellen. But Miles stayed back by camp. He barked at me. I always listened to Miles. When I came over, his snout pointed at a honeycomb pipe.

I heard laughter in the wind, and felt an overabundance of wonder.

TOWN

We followed the road back to town to pick up more dog food for Miles and books for me. Right as we were pulling out of the supermarket, Mary-Ellen stuttered, an extremely unusual behavior, and all of my senses turned on in a different way. Across the street from the market was a Mom 'N' Pop looking auto shop, oddly enough.

I was experiencing a profound sense of déjà vu.

A young man, well, a boy really…he couldn't have been more than sixteen, greeted me. He was pimply-faced, but looked strong and had kind, inquisitive eyes—a similar shape and color as mine. "How can I help you, brother?" he asked. I saw that he wore a silver cross around his neck.

"I have a 1969 Mustang Mach 1 Cobra Jet sitting out over by the market across the way—and I suppose the carburetor finally kicked the bucket," I said. "It was original after all..."

The boy peered out of the garage doors, into the white-light heat of New Mexico. He saw Mary-Ellen sitting there, heat waves exploding off of the stark black of her body. Her lines cut the horizon like a knife through a warm pad of butter. The boy unconsciously clutched at his cross.

Suddenly, the air in the room had shifted. The smell changed. At first it was all oil and gasoline, and the promise of rust. Now, though, there was a very distinct smell hanging in the air, a smell I knew very, very well. I heard a body move in space behind me, but when I turned around—no one was there, and before I could inspect things further, the boy said, "I'm Will, by the way," and he extended his greasy, pretty hand out to meet my own.

Will and I towed Mary-Ellen across the street—we didn't want to strain her. We popped open the hood and tapped on the metal of her guts. We gave her a good inspection. She must've felt very naked.

"Definitely the carb," we said in unison.

The boy scratched the back of his neck, "Well, I can call this in—piece of cake, but it'll take about a day for it to arrive from Denver." We were standing back in the garage when it happened again.

A light in the back of my head switched on now. All the hairs on the back of my neck stood up, my palms turned cold and sweaty and my chest radiated heat, a sick-calm feeling took control of my nervous system. A delicate hand set down a red bowl filled with cool water in front of my dog, in slow motion.

I followed that hand up the arm, past the shoulders and back up the neck.

"I like your dog," she told me. "He looked thirsty. I hope that's alright."

Will, who was in the back of the shop making a call, waved to me and smiled.

I looked at this woman slack-jawed, and managed to say, "Yes, fine, thank you."

The woman, who smelled like shea butter (that was the smell!) stared into my eyes. "You look so familiar to me, what's your name?" she asked.

"Will," I replied.

She slapped her thigh, and let out a laugh that sounded like bells. "What a coinkydink! That's my son's name! But I guess you already knew that..."

She moved over to my Mary-Ellen and ran her hand along the body of the car, "You have really nice things." She peeked into the back seat and saw the neat stack of local newspapers piled halfway up the back of the driver's seat, along with blankets and a suitcase. "It looks like you lead an interesting life."

"You could say that, I suppose." I was looking down at the ground, unable to think straight. I wanted to run into this woman's arms; I felt so small and could feel the bruises of early childhood begin to pepper my knees again; I could taste the certain, not-quite-vanilla of soft serve ice cream cones; could remember the exhilaration of catching fireflies in the palm of my hand, and then releasing them back into the world.

"I'm sorry that I'm staring, you just seem so familiar to me. Are you a god-fearing man, Will?"

"Not fearing, no."

"But you are a believer?" she probed.

"I believe in something bigger than our own conception of ourselves and the universe, and I don't have a problem referring to whatever that force, or thing, may be as God." I looked down at my feet very seriously, "Succinctness of language is important to me."

She mulled over what I had just said, and a funny sort of pained expression took over her face, "I was a wanderer too. Many years. I left people very precious to my heart but I could never be the new person I was becoming in the place where I was at. And though I was sorry that I had to leave, I'm not sorry that I had to find me." Her eyes filled with tears, and what I mistook for extreme earnestness at first now looked to me like something wasn't quite right behind her eyes. "And it was no coincidence that in finding myself...I also found God, and Jesus Christ our Lord and Savior. Do you know what that's like? Finding yourself like that? I bet you do."

I stopped to consider her words, "Yes ma'am, I do."

Will came over to us and informed me the new part was "sure-fire on its way, and would be ready to install at eight-thirty a.m. tomorrow." The woman, upon hearing my intentions to sleep in my car, said she wouldn't dream of letting me do such a thing when she had an extra room to spare. I assured her that it was quite alright, and that I was very accustomed to sleeping in my car. But she persisted, and a very big part of me wanted to stay with her, and the boy (Will!) who so resembled me. So, I did.

Their home was filled with blue things. But not sad blue—the bright blue of southwestern turquoise, and Dominican ocean azul. The woman pulled together the most delicious and nostalgic meal I had tasted in many, many years. The flavors filled me with a warm mixture of delight and sadness.

We three sat at the dinner table for hours. We spoke about weather, horses, different ways to tie knots, the Oxford comma, violins, cars, the simplicity of roads, Jack London, prehistoric sea-dwelling creatures, our favorite smells and physical feelings: Will liked to dig his feet into cool sand; the woman liked scratching fresh mosquito bites; I said I liked dancing the most.

The boy crawled into bed around three a.m. "See you in the morning for quick work, brother," he said with tired lips.

"Good night," I replied.

The woman and I stayed up talking all night. Neither of us blinked.

It was eight a.m. somehow and the boy was in the shower again—had he been in there this whole time? Flow had taken over my perception of things in the dark of night, but now that we were again bathed in the white light of Southwestern summer—time swooped back in through the window, riding the coattails of first light.

The woman got up from the table for the first time and went over to the counter to make coffee. She pulled out a mason jar of very dark, whole beans from the freezer. The whiteness of her hands against the jar of brown coffee is an image I return to when I feel unsure. She ground the beans down for auto drip, poured the water, and turned the machine on. "Will," she began, "We've been talking for nearly twelve hours and I still don't know where you're from."

I hesitated, but only slightly, "A small town in Western Massachusetts."

"Get out of town. Me too!"

She poured us two cups of strong, black coffee.

"And how old are you? Do you have a wife?" She looked at my left hand. "I guess not, but you never know. People's lives are always more complicated than they seem from the outside."

The woman sat down next to me and looked at me real hard. She put her hands on my face and ran the back of her right index finger against the grain of my beard.

"You should find a wife. Companionship is the most important thing in the world next to faith. Family is the thing, you know."

I put my hand on her wrist very gently and moved her arm away from my face.

"Which town did you say you were from, again?"

The pipes in the old wood and brick apartment in a small town in New Mexico made a slight screeching noise. The boy, wrapped in a white cotton towel, stepped out of the bathroom.

"Would you mind if I had a shower?" I asked gingerly. "I can't remember the last wash I had standing proper."

As soon as the water rolled down my chest, I heaved great, celestial waves of sadness into my hands. The magnetism of this place, and that woman (my mother!) overrode my brain. My inability to cry was washed away with my tears, down the drain. I sobbed sitting cross-legged on the floor of the porcelain tub. I cried for the little girl that the woman would never see again; I cried for the woman and her weakening mind, trying desperately to place me; I cried for the boys in the world who would never know a father; I cried for Natasha and the Children of the Sun; for Owen and Amy. I cried for everything that hurt. I wanted to become a part of the water running down my body. I wanted a part of me to cling to the squeaky pipes in that apartment forever. I wanted to stay with the woman and the boy, and have her braid my hair, and cook me food and teach me about the Earth again like she used to. But she wasn't of the Earth anymore. She was a pupil of the Word, and her mind was beginning to wander. The frost had come into her hair early.

I wanted to be part of something bigger than just me. But it was already eight-seventeen a.m., and I had a boy waiting for me downstairs with a car part in his hands.

BE HERE NOW

The road seemed to me now completely explored. I loved it still, but longed for something I could not name. I drove back east some ways to Louisiana. Back to New Orleans. I couldn't tell if I was retracing my steps in the hopes of uncovering some unknowable answer kept hidden from myself, or if I was just driving.

I pulled down a stretch of road that used to make my heart skip a pump or two—rattling my rib cage in the process. I had to pull over because the sensation I was experiencing was unlike anything I had ever felt before. Excitement and dread. A cold sweat started in my left ventricle, and spread up and over my upper lip. I could actually feel the blood pumping in my heart. I was afraid if I swallowed that I would induce cardiac arrest. But the moment passed. I drove further down the road, to the cul-de-sac. The apartment complex to which I once held keys looked different to me now. A new coat of paint perhaps? I knocked on the door of the apothecary shop.

A young man with bright red hair and a long nose that silver framed spectacles rested on answered the door. "Hullo there! We closed for the evening, and on Sundeys. But Triangle Books will reopen at nine a.m. Monday morn'n, and we'll be extra pleased to see you again then. G'night, friend." The young man saluted me with two outstretched fingers, and began to close the door after him.

"Wait!" My voice cracked, "Is Natasha around, do you know?"

The young man leaned on the doorframe, and looked at me differently now, "How do you know 'Tasha?"

I was silent. How didn't I know Natasha? Baby powder and shea butter, right? I had no idea how to respond.

He stepped past the door, and looked me very honestly in the eye, "Look here, Natasha died a few years back. She was a good friend of my family. She left us her spread. Are you Will?"

I nodded.

"You best come inside…" He sighed.

The shop, which was once filled with jars of leaves and vials of delicate smelling oils, and small, magical quiet items, was now filled with words. Old books that smelled like cake batter. It was the only time in my life I was ever so sad to see a library.

The young man led me through the bookshop, and upstairs to the apartment Natasha and I once shared. We walked up the old spiral staircase I once lost my footing on.

"People stopped coming for remedies when Natasha got too sick herself to cook 'em. Not cuz they didn't trust her you see, but because she just couldn't make 'em."

I sat in the same chair I had inhabited a decade-and-a-different person ago as the young man made us a pot of tea.

"Didn't have the strenth anymore. But strenth wuddn't everything. No matter who she taught to cook, no hairs sprouted on ol' Ben the baker's balding head no more. No bleeding gums were set right, and not a tummy ache was cured with a ginger candy quite as fast no more. Natasha could fix any and everybody… just not herself. And when she passed, we had to figure out what to do with…not just her stuff…but the shop part of the spread…"

I considered how funny it was to hear this man's thick, humid accent contrasted by his Gaelicness. I looked at the book on the table. He was reading The Foam of the Daze.

"That book can only be read in circles," he called out. I caught the edge of a page the wrong way and my thumb smarted. I sucked the blood off. My hands were the hands of someone manifested into reality. I was—at that moment—my past, my present, and my future. I watched the blood rise to the surface of the slit, and make a perfect, red circle at the base. The young man looked over at me from the kitchen. He told me that he, his family, and some other very close friends of Natasha's agreed that it wasn't right to put her under the ground. They all built a raft out of tree branches, loaded it full of Natasha's leaves, herbs, and beautiful items of power, and laid Natasha's body on top of the raft. Then they lit it on fire at the mouth of the Gulf. Her loved ones gathered on the shore. They watched the raft drift out into the ocean until it was just a black speck on the horizon, with tendrils of smoke rising up towards God, and then nothing. He said the sky turned a wild shade of purple for a week after that.

The young man bent down to pat Miles, who was grateful for his touch but too tired. All he could do to show his gratitude was smile. The man sat opposite me and blew onto the lip of his mug. I looked around and saw Natasha everywhere. She was in the painting of two black girls playing in the river; she was in the lamp that was spreading light around the room so gently; she was in my cup and in my hands.

"Natasha said you might be coming back here 'round this time. Said your stars are very literal. She said she didn't know when abouts exactly, but she also said it would only be when you wanted to rest."

"How did she know that?"

"I don't know how she knew half of the curious things that she did. Do you?"

I shook my head, and laughed. "Natasha knew how to speak to things unseen, and I knew how to listen. Or I did…once upon a time, anyway."

"You blocked?" He pushed his spectacles back on his head with his forefinger.

"No, I still mash those herbs together. I found the seeds years ago."

The young man gave a chuckle, "I don't mean your shitting cycle, I mean your soul, friend. Your soul's out of joint. Your feet walk forwards, but your mind…" He put his hand above the top of his head and wiggled his fingers around, "—it lingers."

I smiled at this strangely accurate motion, "Yeah, something like that."

The young man got up to wash his hands. He applied a dollop of soap and sang "Happy Birthday" quietly to himself, three times.

"They say the amount of time it takes to kill all the germs on your hands is three go-rounds of "Happy Birthday to You.""

Natasha said I was always getting myself sick-like when we were kids cuz I never let myself get dirtied up."

"Dirt exposes, I suppose," I replied.

"Natasha said when you did come back here—that you'd feel stuck, that you woulda grown tired of the very thing that once sustained you."

I mulled over what he had just told me. I thought I should know what he meant, but I was drawing blanks. He then walked to a wooden box on the bookshelf opposite the window. He gingerly opened the lid and pulled out an envelope and a set of keys (keys!).

"Said if you ever come back, and in all likelihood you was going to, said to give you these." He laid the items down in front of me. "Said to tell you to be sure to load up on oranges. Citrus." He paused. "Natasha was very fond of you, you know."

"What does that mean?"

"About the oranges? Beats me, friend."

SOMEWHERE BEYOND THE SEA

Her letter —

> *Will, I told you you would never see me again. It was always hard being right with you. I so liked feeling wrong because the world's too full of questions to feel right all the time, but you made it so easy! Not cuz you had an overabundance of wrong, see, but because you were too smart in your way. You would get overwhelmed by your mind, and do things wonky.*
>
> *You must be wondering what those keys you're holding are to. Well, I'll tell you from beyond the grave (look up at the moon, baby)—You best walk down to South Shore Harbor. Third boat in from the left—the red one is yours now. That boat was my daddy's, and I never took you to it because I thought you'd die if you saw the sea up close. No lines, just an endless number of directions. But I figured if you ever got stuck or confused enough to come back and see me—that you might be tired of lines.*

The next morning, I played chess with the young man. We stalemated twice before we moved on to cards. He shot the moon, so I lost. I asked him if he wouldn't mind letting me keep Mary-Ellen in the garage for a while. When he asked me how long, he laughed and hit his forehead with his palm, "Never mind, dumb question. Yeah, she can sleep here. But I'd be a rotten soul if I didn't tell you that things that stay there…get old real fast somehow. Can't explain it myself. Just happens."

I called Miles to the door, but he just lifted his head.

"I don't think pup wants to go where you're going."

"You're probably right, he must be tired of traveling."

"So must you be, friend."

"I'm not sure what I'm tired of. It's something—but it's not of moving."

"I'll watch him for you whilst you're on your adventures at sea," he assured me.

"Much obliged." New Orleans gets in your tongue when you're there.

I spoke to Miles privately, and then gave the young man a check for dog supplies and a caretaker's fee.

Mary-Ellen idled neatly into the garage. Some part of her seemed to sigh as she moved across the ground towards cover. Her wheels spitting out tiny pebbles behind her, her body relaxing. All of the things I loved seemed to be tired, but not me. A fire burned still in my chest and in my legs. I felt a profound sense of harmony when I didn't know where I was going. The fluids that ran up and down my spinal column would sing.

At Fisherman's Wharf, I looked for the red boat from Natasha's letter. Third one in. Her name was Child of the Sun. A young black child watched me laugh and he started laughing too! He knew exactly why I was giggling and it reminded me of another lyric from my youth, about how babies cry because they feel the world.

A harbor master stood, trying to wind a stubborn wooden handle into the head. "You and my grandson have the same sense of humor it would seem." He pointed at Child of the Sun, "That vessel hasn't moved from that spot since I was his age." The little boy was smashing the abandoned exoskeletons of various crustaceans with a mallet. The harbor master grumbled when he saw this, lay down his hammer project, and marked something down in the open notebook to his left.

"There are some lessons you learn, and some lessons you don't never learn," he said as he picked up the hammer, slammed down on a crustacean and sucked the leg of a crab directly. "I've learned very well that what's passed is past, but I still don't know what the hell people mean when they say to get out of your head. Now tell me how you supposed to get out your damn skull?!"

It was a good question.

"Man, that's another perfectly good mallet I'm gonna have to fix. That baby is mallet-crazy!"

One of those novelty clocks you normally find in kitsch motels, woodworker's shops, and schnitzel houses hung directly above the harbor master's head. Just as I noticed it, the clock struck noon. Instead of a bird sliding out of a hidden compartment, a rather garish, red crab wearing an eyepatch came out and made clacking noises as the claws danced. The whole scene lasted ten seconds, but the harbor master chuckled, clearly delighted.

ISLANDS

For what felt like two weeks straight, I felt dizzy standing up, sitting down, bending over, lying still. I was on a 1953 Chris-Craft Commander Cruiser. There was a single mast that had been hand-built after manufacturing for some reason, which I taught myself how to operate rather quickly. It came in handy as I couldn't get my eyes to focus on a trail of words in the manual without retching. Once I had my sea legs under me, I learned how to operate the engine, but found that I much preferred the calm connection to the wind that the makeshift sail provided. There is a satisfaction that comes with resting into nature that no amount of engine hum can compete with. It was one of the surprising things I was learning about myself in this quietude of vastness.

On cloudy nights, when the moon was hidden, I had no one to talk to at all. I shouted an endless series of "Hello!" and "Can anybody hear me?!" into the empty distance to make sure my vocal cords still knew how to vibrate. With me were six crates of oranges that I kept frozen in the hull, a radio, a sketchbook and pencils, a sweater, three shirts, two pairs of jeans and one pair of canvas shoes. The boat consisted of a main deck, master's quarters with a very comfortable full bed, a full bathroom with a standing shower, kitchenette with a single stove burner, and a spacious hull for storage. It was more than enough space—my own world, compact and contained.

I sailed south and swam in crystal clear waters with sea creatures so happy I could've sworn I caught a few smiles. I would anchor thirty yards away from tiny, uninhabitable islands and swim ashore, my sketchbook and journal both wrapped in plastic. Some islands were so small I was afraid to fall asleep fearing imminent death by encroaching seas. These nameless stretches of land kept me occupied for a day or two each, and I drew all of them, thinking of my mother and her youth. Some only had a single palm tree. I tore out a sheet of paper and wrote down the name of whichever island I had "discovered." There was Bernadine, Rosalie, Q, Jane Doe, Juliet, and Alexia, and more that I can't recall but are written down somewhere. I fashioned crude weapons out of the natural resources of my temporary homes, and crawled back into the sea to gather simpler creatures to eat.

My skin was almost how I remembered Natasha's. I couldn't remember the last time I had spoken words to another human being. I forgot how money worked or what it was. I forgot about conventions and rules of etiquette. I forgot about roads. I had rewilded. The only connection to the larger, busier world was my radio, which—during all of my years at sea—only stayed tuned to the girl and boy groups of the late 50's and 60's. Doo-wop and Motown, that is all you need to survive.

I loved the islands. I loved them completely but I had exhausted myself of tiny spits of land and lonesome fires. The moon and I agreed that it was time. I set my sail to catch the reaching wind that was to take me back to communication.

WATER

At night, I considered my body. I had no looking glass but the windows of my cabin adequately reflected a more ghostly, but most likely, more accurate representation of myself as I was then. My face—now so angular where it was once soft and round— was perpetually wind-kissed and dark. Wrinkles were creeping around my eyes and mouth. My body retained its dancer's form, and the hair on my chest crept down towards my belly like an upside-down vase. I couldn't wrap my head around the idea that this ghostly form peering back at me through a backdrop of glass and stars was a representation of the man I had become, of the man I had Willed into existence.

I missed contact.

How long had I been observing myself? Was it not just night outside? It would appear I had missed a great many sights while I observed my own reflection. I climbed out of my quarters and up to the deck when I saw I was back within the realm of large swaths of land, and the straight lines that traced them. A sense of thirst crept up my throat to steal my attention and I immediately wanted a very cold beer.

That first peek of land I saw was Key West with Route 1 stretched up the middle into Florida proper. I set my course for the Gulf, and turned back to my quarters to begin to pull together the life I had led on the sea for so long.

But there was nothing to pack, just a few items to stick into my canvas bag, now satisfyingly sun-bleached and rusted at the latches. Really the only things outside of my clothes to sort were the stacks of papers and journals I had filled during my island explorations. I took one from the pile that had an intricately-shaded nautilus shell on the khaki-colored cover.

Island Bernadine —
I wonder if this is something my mom would do. I have vague memories of her describing various ocean-faring adventures, but they seem to have faded into outlines in my mind.

Island Q —
The elegance of water is overwhelming. The sun has been set for the last handful of hours and the moon is sending ten-thousand little moons skipping across the horizon. In the beginning, it must have rained for thousands of years, filling all of the places that were deep and dangerous so that creatures wouldn't fall to their death…I stopped for a sip of water after writing that sentence and am now struck by how this water has likely passed through the body of countless other beings before me and will stretch forward the same way. I have to find a way to thank Natasha for this.

Isle Lilith —
Today was a wading day. The Island of Lilith is nothing more than a sandbar. A shallow spit of sand—perfect for wading. I floated on my back—the sun was shining so kindly on my face, my stomach. I could feel all the bad feelings. The confusion and rage that lived in my shadows were now bouncing around inside of me. The sun started to heat them up, bring them up to the surface of my consciousness—of my body. And then I dunked myself. I did this so many times I lost count, but I feel very light now.

Reading back the words of these previous versions of myself, I felt inspired to write. To capture these last hours alone at sea.

My last few days at sea —
I have the look of a man who has grown too accustomed to silence. This can't be good for the soul of any primate. I desire connection…and sugar! Oh god, sugar.

I felt very heavy suddenly, thinking about how badly I wanted a giant slice of banana cream pie. I looked up at the moon shining down at me. My pen was quiet for some time and I reviewed all of the celestial images that came streaming into my inner vision. I picked the pen back up.

> *It's only just occurred to me that I haven't seen another human for over a year. It's also just occurred to me, under the tip of America—how truly terrified I've been of other people.*

I got up from my seat, lowered the ladder on the stern, and stepped into the warm evening water.

HOMESICK

I docked the Child of the Sun back in the third port of Fisherman's Wharf. The laughing child was still hitting skeletons of sea-creatures with one of his grandfather's mallets and still about three years old. I guess flow is subjective, or is it that time's relative? My mouth was very salty, and I just focused on that, because I started feeling dizzy.

The harbor master was picking his teeth with a small stick when I approached him. The white, open cabin that acted as his office with a key-loaded pegboard looked just how I remembered it.

"Well, you got mighty dark mighty quick!" he exclaimed. "Older around the eyes too! The sea will age certain folks quick, I 'spose."

I looked at him, completely perplexed.

"Boy, close your mouth, or the devil may crawl in through your gums, and then you'll be in real trouble."

I shook my head. "I'm sorry, I don't mean to sound strange—but would you mind telling me how long I've been gone for?"

He looked me in the eye, very solemnly and said, "What sea-witch cast her spell on you, I wonder? Let me see your hands, boy." I obliged, and gave him my hands. My head was spinning, but I felt strangely calm. He folded my hands over in his own, and pressed his fingertips to the skin of my palms. He made a lot of grumbling noises to himself. After a long while he gave me my hands back. They felt cold, and I rubbed them together vigorously.

"You've been gone for a couple few hours," he said.

The walk back to Natasha's was the most surreal experience of my life. Sometimes we can play out years of fantasy in our mind's eye. How do we know what's real and what's happened versus what's just our mind's dreamings? And what about the journals filled with writing? I guess it was true that they didn't have dates to mark the passage of time, but there were five full volumes…how?

To see the world in a grain of sand.

It felt as if I had aged five years in body and soul, and yet the collection of my years in reality was a matter of only a couple few hours. The people passing me by on my journey back to the apothecary shop—no, the book shop—all stared at me. I felt like my blood was traveling backwards in an attempt to make sense of the information I had just received. The buildings around me all seemed somehow larger and more colorful than I recalled. I heard live music. I had forgotten how important real, living rhythm was to me.

I followed the sound. A soul group was playing a melodic, but complicated tune. My feet began to tap, then my knees rocked back and forth. Before I was aware of what was happening, I had a young woman in my arms, and we were dancing in the center of a semi-large crowd. People were laughing and clapping along.

Bam.
Bam.
Bam.

Syncopation; mathematics in real time; the flashing whiteness of happy grins; a warm afternoon; the promise of sweat. In the white-hot center of that crowd, I was revived. I knew myself again, and I longed to see my home.

~

A forest had grown over the steel of her body. Vines had wrapped themselves all the way around her. Small trees were growing everywhere. Mary-Ellen was asleep. I felt a hand on my shoulders. The young man, with his red hair and silver spectacles, was there holding an axe and an enormous pair of shears.

"I told ya, time gets funny in there," he said.

"Time is funny everywhere, I guess. I just want to go home."

"I hear ya, Will." He looked at Mary-Ellen. "Looks like you remembered your ruby slippers."

We spent the better part of that day—it must've still been that same Sunday—cutting through nature to reach machine, which we both agreed was metaphorically opposite, but sometimes that's okay.

I wiped Mary-Ellen down as the young man went upstairs to fetch Miles and the check that I had written him.

"Will?"

"Yes?"

"Never mind."

We shook hands and smiled at one another.

"Ah!" he exclaimed, "Natasha, was right about you! You do glow when you smile."

THE BLUE BASEMENT

Sheer exhilaration. Miles and I were coasting down a lonesome stretch of freshly laid road that extended forever. I was screaming at the top of my lungs. Screaming at the road in front of me and at the ghosts behind me. No one and nothing could touch me because I was just a black streak against the horizon. I wanted full volume. I wanted to cut a hole through time and space with my body, my radio, and my car.

I moved through Mississippi, up through Tennessee, and into Kentucky without stopping. In New York I had to stop, something felt familiar. I felt the presence of a lost love, but I was completely alone. I was completely alone again in the real world. I slept. I slept so good that I kept waking myself up to revel in the complete comfort of my own body.

I woke up, what felt like years later. I readjusted my rearview mirror and caught a glimpse of my reflection. My hair seemed fuller, the deep wrinkles that had entered around my eyes and mouth were only shadows now. My skin was again an olive-white with a hint of deep red flowing up and down and back and forth. Time caught up with itself, I guess. Or did I slow down to meet it? I had found a wormhole.

I kept driving east, and suddenly I was back where I had started so many years ago. The house was all boarded up. Thousands of years of fallen leaves caked the yard. The roof had fallen in on the right side. The windows were all busted up from rocks thrown by the small hands of local kids who needed to destroy what was destroyed long ago.

I pulled off the soggy, termite-infested cross-section of wood barring against potential intruders, which I found completely ridiculous. The house was clearly haunted. The interior still smelled like camphor and mildew—unsurprising. I felt only the briefest glimpse of nostalgia before I remembered the cross that the boy wore, and the pipes somewhere in New Mexico. And then I felt a mix of jealousy and gratitude.

In the kitchen, I looked at the counter-top where countless pieces of toasted bread had been smothered in butter and grape jelly. I heard something—a soft buzz of "peas and carrots." I followed my ears down the stairs to the basement. It occurred to me then that I had never once set foot in that basement. An awkward sensation crawled up the front and down the back of me, attacking the joints of my hips, and wrapping itself around my spinal column. I was deeply afraid. I put one foot in front of the other, my body remembering how to wade in the water, accepting any form, any fate, and my own nature.

The source of the noise was an old tube television blasting some program I knew from youth about four sort-of friends who pointed out things about life to each other with great humor and cynicism. I turned it off.

"HEY!"

My heart hit the wall. I turned around. An impossibly gray-haired, shriveled up old man was sitting in a dilapidated, La-Z-Boy recliner, which was crawling with all manner of insects. It was Peter. He carefully pulled the creatures off as they traveled along his arm.

"Hey!" he shrieked again, "I was watching that!"

I walked over to him, and kicked his La-Z-Boy recliner to scramble the insects out of it. They all left. Troves of spindly, many-legged creatures.

"Well, that was really un-cuh-called for don't you think?" Peter was working himself into a fit, "Fuh-First you shut off my program, then you kick my chair. Who do you think you are?"

"I'm Will."

"I-I don't know any 'Will,' and th-this isn't your house, so get out!"

"That chair was crawling with bugs," I said calmly.

He sat the remote down on his lap and clenched his fists in the most heart-wrenching manner I had ever witnessed.

"They were my fuh-friends," my father said through clenched teeth. "You kicked my chair." Full volume, "And you scared m-my friends!" Peter launched himself out of the chair, but his knees buckled out from underneath him, and he collapsed onto the cold cement of the basement. His long, gray, matted, disgusting hair fell over his shoulders. He was wearing a lavender-gray faded robe which was just as unclean as the rest of him.

"Peter...?" I asked softly.

A flicker of recognition spread across his face but immediately disappeared. He sat up slowly and began to cry, crossing his legs, and resting his elbows on his knees.

"I don't know where I am!"

"You're in the house," I said.

"The h-house." He looked up at me instead of through me for the first time.

"I know you," he said. "I know you, man. You used to work on my car a long time ago when I still had a ca-car. You never charged me."

I nodded.

His face lit up, "You're buh-Big Bill's son. I kn-know you, man." He laughed and pointed at me with a long, dirty fingernail. I suppressed a rising tide. I wasn't sure how to feel.

"I know you!" he sighed, "I've been here a long time. I've been underground a la-long, long time. They——" he pointed to the outside world, "They, they knew I was on to them! They knew I had c-c-cracked it."

"Cracked what?"

"It! It! I had solved the space-time continuum problem that had evaded quantum physicists and applied m-m-m-mathematicians for years!"

"How?"

Peter narrowed his eyes and looked hard at the floor, "But they didn't like the idea of some blue-collared, fuh-factory worker wino solving the world's largest problem."

"I didn't know it was a problem..."

"Don't be ridiculous! It's the only problem. Suh-Space." He put his hands out in front of him about twelve inches apart, vertically. "And time," he shifted his hands horizontally.

"How did you solve the problem?"

He motioned at me with his index finger, curling it in towards himself. "Take a nuh-knee, and I'll tell you, because God doesn't like when you bear his secrets s-standing upright. To name a thing—is to take the mystery out of it, you see."

I knelt.

He began, softly, his eyes dancing wildly. "When you lay your head on the ground for a long enough amount of time—you begin to see things sideways." He uncurled his finger, and his mouth widened—he was missing over half of his teeth, and the remaining few were all the color of dirt.

I stayed in the basement with Peter for a number of painful hours. I finally convinced him to come upstairs with me. I told him they believed him now, that they were willing to talk with him, and iron it all out. But that we would need to make him look presentable because the people he was going to be talking to were going to want him to look as good as his theory.

Peter looked nervous as we stood in the bathroom, which had somehow remained absolutely pristine, as if neither time nor neglect had been let inside. The shower was streaming down warm water as I peeled Peter's robe off of his body. He was so like a child. The naked old man stepped under the tap, "Ow! Ow!"

"Is the temperature alright?"

He said that it was and smiled at me. Years and years of filth fell from his body. I told him to sit down in the tub. I plugged the drain and turned on the faucet. I emptied some shampoo underneath the small tumult of water to make bubbles.

"That fuh-feels good," he said, slinking into the tub.

I scrubbed my father and bathed him in soapy water, then washed his filthy hair. I toweled him off and sat him down on a stool. We heard a loud bang from another part of the house. He looked at me through the mirror, "It's all going to be g-gone soon. It knows I'm here now," he said fearfully.

"Yes, it knows but we don't care, do we?"

"No!" he shouted, "No, we don't cuh-care!" I sat him back down. He giggled as I cut his hair with kitchen scissors. I cut his fingernails, and told him to stay still until I came back. He looked scared so I told him to time me, and I dashed out of the house, back to Mary-Ellen.

I dressed him in an old pair of my light blue jeans and a white button-down shirt. He was so skinny that the shirt sort of slouched over his thin frame. But the man standing before me now looked nothing like the troll I had discovered hours ago in the basement. He looked at himself in the mirror.

"I look sharp." He grinned a toothless grin, "They'll— they'll—they'll like me in this."

We heard another loud bang emanate from somewhere deep in the house. I slapped my forehead when I saw his toothless face. He said we had better go before we got squished. I told him we had to do one last thing first. I rummaged through the drawers of my old bathroom.

"I know it's here…"

I found what I was looking for in the closet underneath perfectly pressed white terrycloth towels from a century ago.

"Here," I said, extending the bottle containing a neon-blue liquid. "Swish this inside your mouth for a full minute."

"I don't wanna," he protested. "That stuff is the color of soup-supernovae and I made it a rule to not let anything alien in my body a la-long time ago."

"I'll do it with you…" I said, hoping to get out of there before the roof caved in on us. But we couldn't leave until he did it. Teeth are so important. I couldn't leave before my father took care of his mouth.

"But who will count?!"

"Okay," I said. "I'll count to sixty, but you have to swish this around the whole time."

"Okay," he agreed, as he snatched the bottle from my hand and shot back the liquid.

"One…" I began.

He spat. And the brownest brown imaginable crept down the drain. Peter screamed and another part of the roof fell down, very, very near to us.

I grabbed his hand and we went flying out of the house to the safety of Mary-Ellen where Miles was barking in the most dramatic fashion. We stood there in almost matching outfits and watched the house collapse in on itself.

"That was a cuh-close one," Peter said out loud. We looked at the space where the house once stood. In their own time, the woods would wipe out all record that there was once a structure there. Good.

"Yeah," I managed to say and put my hand on his shoulder instinctively. I looked at him, and for a brief moment, another wave of recognition filled his eyes.

BOTH OF THEM, SETTLED

I slid a check over to a very nice woman behind a desk and said, "I'm sorry we didn't have any papers. I appreciate your gracious assistance with this matter."

"Chicken, we're all zero's and one's now—we don't need to hurt any more trees to find ourselves. It's quite alright, I assure you."

I said goodbye to Peter, who was busy playing checkers with his new best friend who introduced himself to me as Lawrence Welk. Lawrence Welk wore three layers of thermal shirts to protect against Scientologists who were conspiring to steal his childhood teddy bear. He only shaved one side of his face, and wore a maroon beanie day and night. He had a good spirit.

"We are on a ship of fools!" Lawrence Welk exclaimed as he pulled on my sleeve. "If you look closely enough…you may even find yourself on board." Peter gave out a hoot. He liked that. They giggled together like a couple of teenagers.

The sun was breaking through the remaining fall leaves, creating wonderfully complex equations of shadows on the ground. I turned back to look at the long-term care facility I had just left my father in.

It was a nice, red-bricked building with ivy crawling along its north face. The ivy had a comforting effect on me. A lone figure in the window caught my eye—it was Peter. He was smiling, but not at me. It was that time of day in the late afternoon, in late fall when the sun plays tricks on the glass of windows everywhere. Peter was looking out into the canopy of the North-American deciduous trees.

I got in Mary-Ellen; both of them settled.

MOUNTAINS

"You may very well be the worst promise-keeper I done ever met in my whole life, you ol' sonuvabitch!" Owen shouted as he walked down the steps of his modern-looking ranch house. We were both joyful, and for a moment—kids again. He lifted me off the level ground, and spun me around a few times—a very pregnant Amy was watching from the porch.

"Gosh, you just love to work in circles, so I'm gonna spin you in a million of 'em!" He set me down and put his meaty hands on my shoulders. Owen's hair had thinned noticeably, and crawled back some ways along his scalp. His once wild locks were now cropped and he now wore his hair close to his head. Aside from the top of him though, Owen still looked just like Owen.

"Jesus, Will, do you age? You look the got-damn same as when we were kids!"

Owen had a very successful animal vet clinic and Amy sold homemade craft-items on the internet. She was seven months pregnant with their first child. Their love looked exactly as it did that night they danced to Roy Orbison for the first time.

We were all approaching our fortieth year at different speeds and somehow the volume of the world had been turned down slightly. The first morning I stayed with them, I woke up in the guest room around four-thirty a.m. I woke up and considered my life very seriously. A magical force of the universe had pulsed through my veins for as long as I could recall, which had kept me in constant motion. Motion, kinesis—that was my control. I had always been sustained by my deeply rooted desire to move my body through space and along time's sloped horizon. The stylish bedside alarm clock switched over its last digit from a four to a five, and at four-thirty-five a.m., something inside me switched over too.

I began to feel very, very sleepy—as if someone had anesthetized me. A rapid succession of life-images flashed in front of me. I dozed off quickly and dreamt of space. I kept hearing Natasha's voice calling "baby," and I smelled pipe tobacco smoke.

"She's coming back to you, baby…"

I felt very warm.

I saw myself as a newborn, wet and sticky—I had a small penis and testicles. I was a little boy—I had never been a little boy before—I was alive with pleasure. I launched rocks into the night; I erected things only to knock them back down. I hugged my mother so tightly I could've choked her to death; I had a wild, irrepressible energy. I was a teenager. A football player. I met a girl. We fell in love. She got pregnant. My energy existed now in my hands for work, and on the belly of my young pregnant bride. I took up the violin. My child asked me how I made my small music box sing so sweet—like Mama's voice. At twenty-four I had a house but I never owned a car—leases being more practical. I had a tender, contented life.

"Be glad you come out the way you did. He only saw life one way forever," Natasha said.

I saw the rings of Saturn. At nine a.m. I woke to the smell of a very dark roast drifting into my bedroom. It was a very lovely way to wake up, and for a moment I forgot where I was.

"By God, Amy, would you look at this…" Owen started. "I've known this heavenly creature since Father was just Uncle time, and have never known him to rise past five-thirty a.m."

Amy handed me a hot mug of hypnotically good-smelling coffee which I sipped gratefully.

For a week straight, my bones felt like iron, my blood like Mercury. Everything gave me motion sickness. The tone in Owen's voice grew more concerned by the day. He said my flame was low. I thought it was funny how I attracted the sort of person, or was attracted to the sort of person, who would describe things like that. I assured him I would be okay. I just had a funny dream. I, of course, still lent a hand with the chores when and where I could—I would never dream of being an inconsiderate guest. That annoyed Amy who told me to just go and rest.

On the eighth day I woke up at a more agreeable, familiar hour. By seven a.m., I was out of the house. I filled a knapsack with snacks, a journal, and spring water, and began walking towards the mountains. It was good to feel the forward movement of my feet again. My blood was churning after a week of stagnation. "Off," I kept hearing in my head.

In all the years of my life, I had always existed for myself, never questioning an instinct, never knowing a single regret. The forward position had sustained me, but now I needed to review my life. And that afternoon, underneath a Douglas Fir tree and near the expanse of a lake, I decided to make my life in Montana. The climate, I decided, was best suited to my constitution and I could stare at the big sky and those complete sunrises for the rest of my settled days.

METAL AND LIGHT

The idea came to me to purchase an old warehouse in Missoula, Montana—thirty minutes away from Owen's spread, but just a little more centrally located. Owen and I spent six months gutting the property and another year renovating it with a team of hired hands. Miles supervised. The warehouse consisted of two floors, thirty-two-hundred square feet each. We used entirely recycled materials: steel from torn down barn roofs, wood from demolished buildings, and we polished the concrete of the original structure ourselves. I wanted a completely open, light-flooded environment.

"All metals are infinitely recyclable," one of the construction workers said to me through a mouthful of ham-and-cheese sandwich. "That's why I love metal. In two hundred years, when this place gets demolished—they can just reuse all this stuff."

I loved watching the changing light in my home. The summer light at eleven forty-four a.m. made the wood of my floors look entirely different than the eleven forty-four a.m. light did in the winter. I hated not being in my home at certain times of day—not knowing what the light was doing to my floors.

A printing press was set up on the first floor of the warehouse. I wanted to be surrounded by words and ideas, and to help release them into the world. I wanted to be around people! I started hosting dinner parties somehow and began to make more friends.

The garage doubled as my workshop and I made sure Mary-Ellen was in perfect running order always…I just didn't have any reason to use her. I lived within walking distance to the market. My commute to work involved a shower, and twenty-five stairs. People came to my house generally to work, converse, or kiss.

"I'm not sure how good I'll be…" a woman from Minnesota said to me one evening as we stood naked in front of one another. She was a reporter for the Tribune, and had interviewed me for a public interest piece she was writing. Something to do with how my genitals related to my vocation? I was disinterested, but she reminded me of Louise, and I wanted to feel young again.

"I like the way you look. Touch me," she continued.

We had clumsy, wine-drunk sex. My body felt heavy and empty at once. When she left the next morning, she said I smelled like a candy bar, and bit my lower lip. She didn't end up writing anything about my genitals, but about the impact of my work. That was right.

She asked me after we stopped touching each other how it was that I wasn't married. She then immediately apologized saying it wasn't any of her business. I told her I thought it was a good question. Of all the questions she had asked me that evening for her article—this personal and holy query was the only one I recall. Maybe we listen better when we're naked. I told her I didn't believe in marriage, but I did believe in the sanctity of being accountable to an Other.

I think that freaked her out a little.

A LOVE LETTER

As had become my Friday morning custom, I woke in eager anticipation of my substantial breakfast on the horizon. It's always been a balm to locate myself by the lightening shades of color dawn provides. In the evening there is feeling, in the morning there is meaning, and early morning rituals have given me a sense of at-one-ness with the world.

What struck me most? That I was now rooted in a place as well. My perception of belonging, once upon a time, had only been reserved for Mary-Ellen. But now, my place in the world spread out in concentric circles, from my home onto the street, and up into the alpine tree line above. Gratitude for being a part of, no longer apart from.

Miles was still asleep at the foot of my bed, white hairs at the tips of his donkey-like ears that were once tinged hazelnut. He grumbled as I gave him morning love pats.

The mercury hovered barely above freezing, not unusual for middle-spring in this particular part of the country. Montana weather afforded me the luxury of layers to protect my body with. This physique, now so much my own, a hard-won landscape of harmony.

My very own feet took me to my Friday morning refuge, a place for the devotees of sizeable breakfasts to worship amongst their own kind. The wind nipped at the bare parts of my face; thankfully there were few, as my winter beard had grown out to its proper length—more homespun protection. Even though the cold numbed the tip of my nose, I could still pick up the Fir and frozen dirt swirling through the air. Each outbreath illuminated white and golden curls of sun and carbon—that same sense I woke up with, of belonging to all things.

My favorite waitress, Geraldine, was serving that morning. A deeply wrinkled woman of unknowable age, she had survived four husbands, and despite alluding to her considerable wealth, chose to work at The Red Onion, my beloved diner stuck in a time long ago.

Geraldine's hands, despite their frequent, soap-induced abuse, were remarkably untouched by age. I loved them, and how her thumbs curved like the body of a guitar. One day, I told her as much. She asked me to stop flirting with her immediately, and proceeded to bring me a plate of flapjacks that I did not order with a playful wink.

As I took my seat, she adjusted her 1960's beehive style, white wig—a half foot or so of synthetic good nature curling up towards god. I wondered what it meant to her.

"Six-thirty." She took a pencil out of the pennant hairdo. "Right on time."

"Geraldine, my joy, and how are you this delightful dawn?"

She licked the tip of her pencil as she always did. "Good. Fine. You sound chipper."

"As much as I love our Friday banter, I have to ask—"

"I do this because I'm here, and have been for years. Besides, if I stopped, I'd have no nosey young men around to compliment my delicate hands." She held her palms out like an old Palmolive hand model.

"I'm not so young anymore. I'm coming up on my forty-fifth year."

Geraldine's usually friendly pencil bumped me on the top of my skull. I looked up at her in complete surprise. "When you're my age, you're going to laugh at what you just said."

I rubbed my head although I barely felt the eraser's blow, "Maybe you're right."

"Of course I am. Now what do you want?"

She cleared away the empty dishes after my meal. I sat back in my two-person booth, the one in the very back corner of The Red Onion, and watched the late-risers arrive in the impossible-to-time rhythms that mark the ebbs and flows of any local diner. Some came alone, paper under the arm to gulp down cup after cup of hot coffee. Those who had made plans with others embraced under piles of clothes, and I found that I very much enjoyed the sound of parkas kissing. What I always found so satisfying was the way Geraldine remained herself with each person, meeting them on their own terms—reading their tone of voice or body language to measure the right amount of interaction each person might be wanting in order to feel a part of the space. I admired her ability to do this and wondered what I would discover about myself the more I let people like Geraldine into my life.

I considered what the rest of my day was going to look like and wondered if Owen had any interest in ice fishing this weekend. His son was getting to be of an age to start teaching things to. Geraldine walked over and placed the check face down, somehow intuiting that my legs were stirring despite having been camped out for hours.

"About that time, huh," she said, topping off my cup of coffee. "How does it, Will?"

"Fine, Geraldine, just fine. I feel very alive."

ACKNOWLEDGMENTS

The following is a humble attempt to acknowledge the people, places, and things that deserve recognition in the context of this work—there are, of course, too many to name.

Forces: I'd like to thank this period of time, and the Jupiter cycle coming to a close that opened with the birth of the first draft in 2012. Thank you to the elements, and the Ocean. Major shout out to my second-house Libran-Mercury without which I'm not sure I'd love writing the way I do. Thank you, Saturn—Spiritual Master, Spiritual Friend. I'm grateful for my analysis, in allowing me to have things. Thank you to all the unseen, unnamed, and unknowable.

Beings: My animals, my friends near and far who have delighted me and given me inspiration for some of these characters. I wish to thank my editor, Jennifer, for giving me the gift of reflection and engagement as well as keen feedback that made this offering what it is. Thank you Albo for DM-ing me PRAVUM UK's handle. Thank you, Yeats for the words, and Mary-Lee Grisanti for gifting me The Complete William B Yeats anthology during my undergrad (which is also quoted in this text from the 1966 printing of Selected Poems and Two Plays of William Butler Yeats, edited by M.L. Rosenthal and published by Macmillan Publishing Co.), and for always championing my work. Thank you to Gary Paulson for planting the seed of this idea in my young mind on a train to Massachusetts in 1997. Thank you, Blue Willow Tea House, I rounded out this story between sips of your tea. I'd like to acknowledge my family lines, and thank all those who made my being here possible—it took many years and many nations, much water, many fires, but I'm so grateful.

And finally, thank you.

ABOUT THE AUTHOR

Oliver Slate-Greene is a surfer, poet, aspiring horseman, and lifelong student of esoterica. He's a fourth generation New Yorker but is much more identified with his California life/style. He holds a master's degree in psychology and works in brand. He is a cat dad of two, both very naughty, whom he is completely devoted to. This is his first novel.